# NORTH AMERICAN APPLES:
# VARIETIES, ROOTSTOCKS, OUTLOOK

# NORTH AMERICAN

# APPLES: VARIETIES,

# ROOTSTOCKS, OUTLOOK

R. F. CARLSON

E. S. DEGMAN

A. P. FRENCH

R. PAUL LARSEN

VIRGINIA MAAS

JAMES B. MOWRY

HOWARD A. ROLLINS, JR.

W. H. UPSHALL

EMERY WILCOX

MICHIGAN STATE UNIVERSITY PRESS

*East Lansing*

1970

*Copyright © 1970*
Michigan State University Press
*Library of Congress Catalog Card Number:* 78-133436
Standard Book Number: 87013-157-5
MANUFACTURED IN THE UNITED STATES OF AMERICA

★
  ★
★
  ★
  ★

# CONTENTS

# PREFACE

The credit for this book belongs to William A. Luce, of Yakima, Wash. who suggested it at the time when he was President of the American Pomological Society (1963-65). The Society gave its approval and the authors were selected for the various chapters. Each author was allowed considerable latitude in treating the subject and, consequently, there is wide variance in style and arrangement. Because this very divergence may be of interest to the reader, I have made minimal changes in manuscripts.

Over the years most apple varieties (cultivars) give rise to *mutations* commonly called *bud sports*. For the most part, they vary only in having more red color on the skin at harvest time. A few of them have more compact growth, terminal growths being shorter, stouter, and with leaves closer together. On older wood the internodes are shorter so that the spurs are closer together. They are known as *spur-type sports* and give a tree about 2/3 normal size. These spur-type sports may arise on the original variety or on one of its high color strains. Sports are considered strains of the original variety, not a new variety, and this is the reason that usually all or part of the original variety name is retained.

Sports always arise from a single bud which has been altered in its genetic composition. This bud grows into a tree, or a limb of a tree, and becomes a *whole-tree sport* or a *limb sport*. If it is the latter, one can be sure that it originated in that particular orchard, the exact time not so easily determined. If it appears as a whole-tree sport, it could have originated as a bud sport in the nursery, or in the orchard from which propagation wood was obtained by the nursery, or even beyond that particular orchard. It is well known that different nurseries sometimes use the same source of propagation material and that they sell trees to one another. Whole-tree sports occurring in various orchards could therefore have a common origin even if the trees were purchased from different nurseries. Very occasionally, if seedlings are used as rootstocks, a desirable new variety can develop if the scion is killed or broken off and the seedling becomes the tree.

W. H. Upshall, Editor
*Vineland, Ontario, Canada*

# ACKNOWLEDGEMENTS

The American Pomological Society is indebted to the authors of this book who willingly and gratuitously agreed to write sections for which they had particular qualifications. Our appreciation goes also to many other professional horticulturists, to several commercial nurseries, particularly Stark Brothers, and to fruit growers and their organizations for information useful to the authors. For help in editing, credit is given to Dr. R. F. Carlson, Department of Horticulture, Michigan State University, East Lansing, Michigan, Chairman of APS Editorial Committee and his associates on that committee, Dr. Roger Way, Geneva, New York, and Dr. J. N. Moore, Fayetteville, Ark.

# NORTH AMERICAN APPLES:
# VARIETIES, ROOTSTOCKS, OUTLOOK

# I. INTRODUCTION

## ARTHUR P. FRENCH

University of Massachusetts,
Amherst, Mass.

THE APPLE HAS BEEN VALUED BY MAN FOR FOOD AND BEVER-
age purposes since very early times. Carbonized apples were
found in the remains of the prehistoric Lake Dwellings of Swit-
zerland. Though the cultivated apple is generally considered to
be a native of the Caspian Sea region, its introduction to the
North American continent doubtless coincided with the arrival
on these shores of the early colonists from Europe.

While some named varieties of European origin were grown
by the colonists, the chief method of dissemination of the apple
in the new land was by seed. Many east coast pioneers carried
apple seeds with them as they moved westward to establish new
homes in the wilderness. The legendary Johnny Appleseed—
born John Chapman at Leominister, Massachusetts, June 26,
1776—was but one of the many pioneers who helped to spread
the apple westward.

During pioneer times a high percentage of the apple crop was
consumed as cider. For this purpose, fruit from these nonde-
script seedling trees was adequate. However, as few of the apple
varieties which were brought across the Atlantic by our ancestors proved to be adapted to the North American climate, there
was need for varieties of American origin to supply apples for
culinary and dessert purposes throughout the season. Among
the unnumbered thousands of seedling apple trees which must
have existed, some were discovered which bore better than

average fruits. Many of them were selected at least for local use and were given names. By no means did all of these selections find general favor but as late as 1872 Downing's *Fruits and Fruit Trees of America* listed and described over 1000 named apple varieties of American origin.

The choice of varieties to plant is one of the first and most important decisions which a fruit grower must make. On this one decision alone may depend the success or failure of his entire enterprise. Hence from colonial times to the present day, the testing of varieties has occupied the attention of every generation of fruit growers and pomologists alike. Before a thriving apple industry could be developed in the United States and Canada, the attention of those concerned had to be directed to the selection, propagation and testing of the many scores of superior chance seedlings which were discovered. Furthermore, it was essential that the results of tests in different regions of the country be coordinated and published for the benefit of all concerned. Thus it was that the American Pomological Society (APS), which sponsors this book, grew out of a national convention of fruit growers held in New York on October 10, 1848 "to promote pomology and the sciences upon which it depends" and is still "devoted to fruit variety improvement." Marshall Pinckney Wilder, a Boston merchant and amateur horticulturist, was one of the founders of the Society and served as its president for 35 years. One of the important contributions of the Society during the first 60 years of its existence was its "Catalogue of Fruit Varieties" which was first published in the *Proceedings of the American Pomological Society for 1848* as a "List of Fruits Adopted by the Convention of October, 1848" and includes only 13 apple varieties. This list was expanded and revised regularly at the biennial meetings of the Society. The last such revision was edited by W.H. Ragan and published as Part II of the Proceedings of the APS for 1909. It also appeared as United States Department of Agriculture, Bureau of Plant Industry Bulletin No. 151, *Fruits Recommended by the Ameri-*

*can Pomological Society for Cultivation in the United States and Canada* by W.H. Ragan, 1909.

During the first quarter of the twentieth century, *The Apples of New York* by S.A. Beach in 1905 and the later New York variety books by U.P. Hedrick as well as his *Cyclopedia of Hardy Fruits* in 1922 and his *Systematic Pomology* in 1925 served as the leading reference books devoted to varieties. However, the APS Committee on New Fruits, under the chairmanship of C.P. Close, regularly reported on new varieties at each meeting of the Society until about 1947. More recently the *Register of New Fruit and Nut Varieties,* compiled by Brooks and Olmo and published periodically in the *Proceedings of the American Society for Horticultural Science,* beginning in 1944, has become the official APS repository for information on new varieties. For the person who desires to obtain propagating wood of the less common apple varieties, a list of sources was compiled by an APS committee and published in its *Fruit Varieties and Horticultural Digest* in 1954. An additional list of sources of apple varieties, rootstocks, and species was published in the same periodical in 1968.

With the present volume, the American Pomological Society continues this tradition by providing up to date information concerning American apple varieties.

# II. VARIETIES OF YESTERYEAR

### ARTHUR P. FRENCH

IT IS NOW WELL OVER 300 YEARS SINCE DISSEMINATION OF the Roxbury Russet—one of the oldest known American apple varieties—began. Beach (2, p. 294) records that soon after 1649 this variety was taken from Massachusetts to Connecticut. According to Taylor (4, p. 311) the earliest known trans-atlantic shipment of an American apple variety was "that of a package of Newtown Pippins of the crop of 1758 sent to Benjamin Franklin while in London." While there are few records for that period concerning the date of origin, it is certain that two other American apple varieties which later gained commercial importance—Baldwin and Rhode Island Greening—were known during the first half of the 18th century. In all probability Ben Davis and Winesap were also grown during that period. Varieties originating during the next one hundred years, 1750-1850, and which became commercially prominent in the present century, include Jonathan, Rome Beauty, Grimes Golden, Maiden Blush, Tompkins King, Northern Spy, McIntosh, and York Imperial. Of our present 15 leading commercial apple varieties only Wealthy, Stayman, Delicious, Golden Delicious and Cortland originated since 1850. With the exception of Cortland, which is the product of the scientific plant breeder, all of these are of chance-seedling origin, mostly without knowledge even of the seed parent.

These are but a few of the many scores of superior chance seedlings discovered, propagated, and grown, in the eastern states and provinces during that great testing period of North

American fruit varieties during the 18th and 19th centuries. A list of the more prominent of the old favorites would certainly include Black Gilliflower (Sheepnose), Blue Pearmain, Bonum, Chenango, Esopus Spitzenburg, Hubbardston Nonesuch, Peck Pleasant, Porter, Rambo, Red Canada, Smokehouse, Sutton, Sweet Bough, Wagener, Westfield (Seek-no-further), Williams and Winter Banana in addition to most of those listed in the 1915 part of Table 1. Names such as Nonesuch and Seek-no-further suggest the high esteem in which these old favorites were held in their day. An incident which occurred at the New England Fruit Show in the early 1920's illustrates the regard with which one of these old varieties was held. An elderly lady on approaching a plate of extra large beautiful Golden Delicious, being exhibited by the introducer of that variety, was heard to exclaim to her companion "There are the first real Porter apples I have seen in years."

Modern commercial apple orcharding with its emphasis on high yield per acre and efficiency of operations, made necessary by ever increasing costs of production, has been responsible for the great reduction in the number of varieties propagated. In all probability the total number of apple varieties offered for sale by all nurserymen in North America today does not exceed 10% of the list of 878 varieties compiled by Bailey (1) in 1892 from 95 nursery catalogues. This elimination of many old favorites has been lamented by many a connoisseur of the apple. The sentiments of that group have been well expressed by Liberty Hyde Bailey (1), the late dean of American horticulturists, in the following quotations from his writings:

"A person has a right to gratify his legitimate tastes."
"There is merit in variety itself. It provides more points of contact with life and leads away from uniformity and monotony."
"To the lover of choice fruit nothing is old; every succeeding crop is as choice and new as is the new year itself."
"Quantity-production will be an increasing source of wealth, but it cannot satisfy the soul."

Individual varieties do have their faults which make them unsuited and therefore unprofitable to grow commercially. Furthermore, with the advent of cold storage and, now, the modern controlled atmosphere technique, the need for a succession of varieties maturing from early summer to late winter has been greatly reduced. In the not too distant past most families bought at least several varieties of winter apples by the bushel—or even barrel—for storage in the dirt-floor cellar of the home.

Just how greatly the list of leading apple varieties in the United States has been changed in the last 50 years may be seen in Table 1 which ranks, percentage-wise, the leading varieties of the 1915 era and those of 1964. The basis of reporting has changed over this 50-year period. In 1915 the *total* apple crop of the country was 230,011,000 bushels (5, p. 488-489) whereas in 1964 the *commercial* apple crop was 140,345,000 bushels (6). However for the following variety observations from this table the change from total to commercial crop is relatively unimportant:

1) With 13.4% of the total crop there must have been about 31 million bushels of Baldwin produced in 1915, whereas the 24.3% of the commercial crop which were Delicious in 1964 amounts to over 34 million bushels.

2) The number of varieties reported has shrunk from 35 in 1915 to 18 in 1964, reflecting the trend toward fewer varieties now in commercial plantings.

3) Delicious, Golden Delicious and Cortland, which were too new to be listed in 1915, account for 35% of the 1964 crop.

4) McIntosh has jumped from no better than 28th in 1915 to 2nd place in 1964.

5) Baldwin, Ben Davis and Gano, a Ben Davis sport, which accounted for almost 28% of the crop 50 years ago, dropped to 2.2% of the 1964 crop.

6) Seven summer varieties—Early Harvest, Maiden Blush, Oldenburg, Red Astrachan, Red June, Yellow Transparent, and Gravenstein—produced 12.8% of the crop then; whereas only one summer variety, Gravenstein, with 2.3% is listed for 1964,

TABLE 1. *Apple Production by Varieties**

| 1915 | | 1964 | |
|---|---|---|---|
| | % | | % |
| Baldwin | 13.4 | Delicious | 24.3 |
| Ben Davis | 13.3 | McIntosh | 13.1 |
| Northern Spy | 6.1 | Golden Delicious | 8.0 |
| Winesap | 5.1 | Rome Beauty | 7.8 |
| Rhode Island Greening | 4.7 | Jonathan | 7.3 |
| Jonathan | 3.6 | Winesap | 5.4 |
| Rome Beauty | 3.1 | York Imperial | 5.0 |
| Early Harvest | 2.8 | Stayman | 4.8 |
| Wealthy | 2.2 | Yellow Newtown | 2.7 |
| Grimes Golden | 2.2 | Cortland | 2.7 |
| York Imperial | 2.1 | Rhode Island Greening | 2.6 |
| Maiden Blush | 2.0 | Northern Spy | 2.6 |
| Oldenburg | 1.9 | Gravenstein | 2.3 |
| Red Astrachan | 1.9 | Baldwin | 1.6 |
| Fall Pippin | 1.7 | Wealthy | .9 |
| Gano | 1.6 | Grimes Golden | .8 |
| Yellow Newtown | 1.6 | Ben Davis & Gano | .6 |
| Limbertwig | 1.6 | Black Twig | .1 |
| Red June | 1.6 | Other varieties | 7.4 |
| Stayman | 1.5 | | |
| Yellow Transparent | 1.5 | | |
| Yellow Bellflower | 1.4 | (1915 cont.) | |
| Tompkins King | 1.4 | | |
| Golden Russet | 1.4 | | |
| Fameuse | 1.3 | | |
| Gravenstein | 1.1 | Missouri Pippin | .8 |
| Tolman Sweet | 1.0 | Arkansas (Black Twig) | .7 |
| McIntosh | .9 | White Pearmain | .5 |
| Wolf River | .9 | Other varieties | 10.4 |
| Arkansas Black | .9 | | |
| Northwestern Greening | .9 | | |
| Horse | .9 | *Percentage of total production | |

and the production of all summer varieties in 1964 was only
4.2% of the crop.

7)  On the basis of percentage of total crop from 1915 to 1964
(Table 1), Jonathan, Rome Beauty, York Imperial, Yellow
Newtown, Stayman, and Gravenstein have gained in relative
importance; Winesap has held steady; while Northern Spy, R.I.
Greening, Wealthy and Grimes Golden have lost ground.

8)  In addition to the first six summer varieties listed above, the
following fall and winter varieties are no longer grown in suffi-
cient quantity to deserve a listing—Fall Pippin, Limber-twig,
Yellow Bellflower, Tompkins King, Golden Russet, Fameuse,
Tolman Sweet, Wolf River, Arkansas Black, Northwestern
Greening, Horse, Missouri Pippin, and White Pearman.

Later chapters of this book will be devoted to full discussion
of the most important commercial varieties of the present time.
However, the minor varieties of the 1964 list (Table 1) and
some of those which have disappeared from commercial listing
since 1915 still merit some individual consideration.

*Baldwin,* originating as a chance seedling in the town of Wilmington, Massachusetts about 1740, was for years known locally as the Pecker or Woodpecker apple because the tree was
frequented by birds of that type. It was called Baldwin only after
Colonel Baldwin (whose attention was directed to it by Samuel
Thompson) began its propagation and introduced the variety
throughout eastern Massachusetts. A granite monument (Fig.
1), topped by a good carved likeness of the apple, marks the spot
near which the original tree stood.

The Baldwin became the leading winter variety of the
Northeast chiefly because of its general adaptability, good color
when well grown, desirability for eating raw, cooking or juice,
satisfactory keeping ability, high productivity, and longevity of
its vigorous tree. It was doubtless responsible more than any
other variety for the familiar saying "An apple a day keeps the
doctor away." However, neither tree nor fruit are without serious weaknesses. The strong biennial—and in some cases even

FIG. 1.  Baldwin apple monument, Wilmington, Mass.
*(Courtesy, A.P. French)*

triennial—bearing habit of individual trees or parts of the tree has made for irregular production, and the occasional severe winters of the northern regions have seriously weakened or killed many Baldwin trees. The greatest weakness of the fruit is its susceptibility to Baldwin spot or bitter pit. These faults of tree and fruit have, alas, been the downfall of this variety, once king of North American apples.

At least two color sports of Baldwin have been discovered and propagated: the Double Red Baldwin which originated in 1924 at Sawyer Orchards, Salisbury, New Hampshire; and the Galbraith Baldwin which was found in 1934 as a small limb sport in the orchards at the University of Massachusetts.

*Ben Davis.* Little is known of the origin of this variety but it doubtless dates back at least to the beginning of the 19th century. As the Baldwin dominated the northern apple belt, so the Ben Davis and its high colored forms, Black Ben and Gano, once ruled supreme in the more southerly apple growing regions. There a longer and warmer growing season brought this variety to its mediocre best but caused Baldwin to become a large, soft, fall apple of poor color.

The tree of Ben Davis is generally vigorous, hardy, comes into bearing early, bears annually, and is abundantly productive. One of the tree's major weaknesses is its susceptibility to nailhead canker disease which usually is fatal. Never known for quality, its attractively striped bright red fruits were extremely firm and would keep under ordinary cellar conditions late into the winter. Because of this firmness, many of them were formerly shipped by bulk in boxcars into the deep South where they were handled by the "scoop-shovel" method. An apple distributor would spot his carload on a railroad siding in some village or city, advertise the fact, and customers would come with their own containers to buy apples at a low price scoop-shoveled from the boxcar floor into their containers. This provided persons of low income with fruit which they could not have afforded to buy if handled through a retail store. Even after the skin has become oily and the fruit overripe it still makes a fairly palatable apple sauce. However, as evidence of its poor quality, the writer can attest to the fact that Ben Davis is the only variety which an instructor can use for a class exercise in grading or packing apples and expect to pick up as many apples at the end of the exercise as he put out at the beginning.

*Fall Pippin.* Although never of great commercial importance, this fine old fall apple was widely distributed in early orchards of the Northeast. A red skin instead of a greenish-yellow one would have given the variety an appearance commensurate with its tender, aromatic, fine quality, yellow flesh. Otherwise both the fruit and the tree have mostly desirable characteristics. Its origin is completely unknown.

*Fameuse.* Usually considered to be of eastern Canadian origin, before 1700, the Fameuse or Snow apple was one of the most important varieties found in commercial orchards of northern New York and Vermont prior to the McIntosh era. It was highly prized chiefly as a fall and holiday dessert apple having attractive red color, tender white flesh, and excellent flavor. Small size of fruit and susceptibility to apple scab are its two greatest weaknesses. The tree is medium in size, hardy and productive, but usually biennial in bearing and not suited to all soils.

*Gravenstein.* Even though this variety is of European origin the small but important niche which it fills in the commercial apple crop necessitates its inclusion in this list. Its fruit is good size, attractively striped when allowed to ripen on the tree, and excellent in quality. For sauce and pies, it is unexcelled in its season. As evidence of that fact, some years ago the writer was informed by the commissary manager of one of the large restaurant chains in greater Boston that, if available throughout the year, they would use nothing but Gravenstein for apple pies. In support of his statement he produced records showing that during the period when they use Gravenstein their daily average apple pie consumption jumped to almost double what it was during the rest of the year.

Unfortunately the weaknesses of the tree are serious. The crop ripens over an extended period of time and drops so readily that many southern New England orchardists have harvested by placing a thick layer of hay under each tree and picking up the fallen apples daily. Those which are unbruised are sold as hand-picked since they show no evidence of having been on the ground. Furthermore the tree is only moderately resistant to winter cold. Several times during the past 50 years many mature Gravenstein trees have been winter-killed in New England.

The variety is still commercially important chiefly in two areas (1) Nova Scotia and (2) California. According to A.D. Crowe of the Research Station, Kentville, Nova Scotia, Gravenstein was brought there about 1835 from the gardens of the London Horticultural Society. By 1875 it had become one of the leading varieties of the province. Presently some 85% of the total production of the variety in Nova Scotia comes from color strains of which the Crimson Gravenstein is the most important.

The Gravenstein reached California about 1820, being one of several apple varieties planted at a Russian settlement near the present town of Bodega in Sonoma County. However, the present Gravenstein acreage around nearby Sebastopol did not get started until about 1863 when William J. Hunt brought young budded trees of the variety from the East. Today this is the leading Gravenstein area, producing about 2.9 million bushels annually. Because of its superior culinary quality, about 92% of this volume is used by processors.*

Possibly no other variety, unless it be Delicious, has been so subject to bud variation involving color. Many apparent limb color-sports have been observed by fruit growers in the

*This paragraph compiled from material supplied by D.C. Alderman, Davis, California.

Northeast at least. A few of them have been propagated and planted in commercial orchards. The first such color-sport to gain prominence was the Banks which was discovered and propagated by C.E. Banks of Berwick, Nova Scotia about 1886. More recently the Washington Red Gravenstein discovered about 1907 by Van Sent V. Whipple, San Juan County, Wash. and introduced commercially in 1924 has become the chief, if not the only, red sport of this variety available in eastern U.S. nurseries. The Rosebrook Gravenstein was discovered by a man of that name at Sebastopol, Cal. in 1920 and introduced in that State in 1925. One other red sport, the Mead Gravenstein, has been recorded in the *Register of New Fruit and Nut Varieties.* It was discovered by R.J. Fiske, Lunenburg, Mass. in 1927 and introduced in 1939. The New York Agricultural Experiment Station at Geneva reports this strain to be superior to others tested there, but in recent years it has contracted the flatlimb virus disease. Crimson Gravenstein apparently was discovered about 1910 by A.S. Banks, Waterville, Nova Scotia.

*Grimes Golden.* Before the advent of Golden Delicious, Grimes Golden was highly prized as a dessert apple in the "Ben Davis" belt, particularly in the states bordering on the Ohio River. A bowl of Grimes Golden and Jonathan made a most attractive display, and good eating too, on the "side-board" or dining-room table in many a midwestern home from harvest time through the holiday season. Pies made from Grimes Golden apples won many a prize at county fairs.

However, the variety has many weaknesses which have contributed to its decline in importance. The fruit tends to run small on older trees, and is subject to serious scalding in storage. The tree is frequently biennial in bearing habit, only moderately vigorous, and is very susceptible to collar-rot.

The variety originated in West Virginia prior to 1800, which was also the state of origin of the Golden Delicious more recently. Nursery trees as well as fruit of the two varieties have so many physical characteristics in common that the writer is led to believe that Golden Delicious could be an offspring of Grimes Golden.

*Northwestern Greening.* Having originated prior to 1872 in Waupaca County, Wisconsin—which is about 50 miles west of Green Bay—this variety possesses great winter hardiness and is an excellent keeper when grown in the north. It never ranked high with commercial orchardists in the east because its fruit quality is distinctly inferior to the Rhode Island Greening. When grown in southern Pennsylvania, the Northwestern Greening becomes a fall variety and is planted there as an early processing variety.

The tree is a vigorous grower, a bit slow to come into bearing, but eventually becoming a reliable cropper, usually biennial. The fruit is large, smooth-skinned, greenish or pale yellow in color, and quite subject to water core especially on young trees.

*Russets.* It is a bit puzzling to find Golden Russet but not Roxbury Russet included in the list of varieties in orchards 50 years ago (Table 1). While both varieties were important in their day, there is little doubt that the Roxbury was the more important of the two from the volume production standpoint. Confusion concerning the identity of both still exists in the minds of some elderly fruit growers possibly traceable to the substitution of one for the other by nurserymen. Even though typical fruits of each variety may be mistaken for the other by the noncritical observer, the trees in nursery row as well as orchard are vastly different, particularly in leaf size, leaf form, and lenticels on young bark.

The day of the russet apple departed with the development of cold storage as both varieties were noted for their long keeping in common storage. However, producers of fine quality sweet cider still like to blend juice from either Russet with that of other winter varieties for distinctive flavor and aroma.

*Tolman Sweet.* This variety was once the leading sweet apple but has gone the way of all truly sweet apples, into oblivion. Few people today know the pleasure of eating a sweet apple raw, baked or combined with quinces into a tasty chunky sauce. Truly they are being deprived, as Bailey might have said, of a soul satisfying experience. The nearest approach to the true sweet apple today is the mild-flavored Delicious variety. Poor color, small size, and lack of market demand are mostly responsible for the disappearance of Tolman Sweet, the origin of which is unknown.

*Tompkins King.* Once in demand as a high quality dessert apple, especially fine for salads, this variety is no longer favored commercially chiefly because of serious weaknesses of the tree. Its most serious defects are shy production, lack of adequate hardiness, tardiness in bearing, very sparse branching, and susceptibility to collar-rot. The fruit frequently is over-size and quite subject to water-core. Apparently having originated near Washington, N.J. the variety was taken to Tompkins County, N.Y. in 1804 for which it was named.

*Wealthy.* Peter Gideon of Excelsior, Minn. planted seed of the Cherry Crab about 1860. One of the resulting seedlings became the Wealthy variety. It gained commercial status not only in that region, where it proved to be winter hardy, but also in many orchard areas throughout North America. The tree is rather small of stature and comes into bearing early which makes it an excellent filler tree. Its desirability as a filler tree caused the variety to be greatly overplanted during second and third decades of this century so that the fruit almost became a drug on the market. The tree is also rather distinctly biennial in bearing. The fruit is attractive, red striped, smooth-skinned and fairly good quality. However the fruit, which matures just ahead of McIntosh, has a tendency to drop badly, and on older trees runs small and is apt to lack color. In regions where McIntosh is the main variety, Wealthy is being replaced by newer varieties which have better fruit characteristics and mature somewhat earlier in season.

One color-sport, Double Red Wealthy, has been registered.

It was discovered by James G. Chase, Sodus, N.Y. in 1933 and introduced commercially in 1940.

*Wolf River.* Here is another very hardy variety from the east-central part of Wisconsin. Beach (3, p. 246) states that it was "Originated by W.A. Springer, near Wolf River, Fremont County, Wis., hence its name." The present writer fails to find either a town by the name of Wolf River or a county named Fremont in any current atlas or Wisconsin road map available. However, there is a village called Fremont, west of Appleton, through which the Wolf River flows.

Besides winter hardiness of tree, the chief merit of this variety is its very large, attractive red fruits. At one time the fruit was in considerable demand for baking. One ingenious Massachusetts fruit grower has used trays of this variety spaced along the roadside on the approaches to his roadside stand to attract attention. Doubtless the widespread mixture of this variety in nursery rows of McIntosh during the late "teens" and "twenties" had much to do with the wide distribution of Wolf River in the Northeast. As that mixture has long since been eliminated from most eastern nurseries and many orchard trees have been either topworked or pulled out, the Wolf River has disappeared as a commercial variety.

*Yellow Bellflower.* The oblong-conic, more or less ribbed fruit with prominent ridges near the apex would distinguish this large, yellow apple from almost any other variety of that color. It was prized more for culinary purposes than dessert, yet after it had mellowed, its rather strong, distinctive flavor was quite acceptable. Apparently it needed a rather mild climate for it developed best in New Jersey, where it originated long before 1800, and in the coastal valleys of California where it was very highly regarded at the beginning of this century. While the tree is vigorous, productive and long-lived, the fruit and foliage are very susceptible to apple scab. Its place has undoubtedly been taken by Golden Delicious.

*Yellow Newtown.*\*Frequently called Albemarle Pippin in Virginia and adjoining areas, this variety supposedly originated in Newtown, Long Island, N.Y. at least early in the 18th century. Being greatly influenced by soil and climate, the Newtown variety developed best in only a few regions: (1) the lower Hudson Valley in New York, (2) the Piedmont and mountain regions of Virginia and North Carolina, and (3) the Pacific Coast States. Because of its very limited adaptability, commercial production of this variety has not materially changed in 50 years. Although it is an attractive, high-quality apple when well grown, its chief merits are firmness of flesh and very late season of usefulness. These features have made it an excellent export variety in the past, but now it is being planted only to a limited extent in the Hood River Valley of Oregon.

Growers started planting Yellow Newtown in the Hood River Valley of Oregon about the turn of the century. During this period and up to the severe freeze of 1919, Yellow Newtown was the leading apple variety there. The Yellow Newtown, which represented about 60% of the total apple acreage prior to the 1919 freeze, declined to approximately 40% during the next decade. Presently, Newtown production is still equal to the total production of all other apple varieties in the Hood River Valley. The variety still meets with ready acceptance as a late keeper for domestic markets. A limited number of young plantings have been established, mainly because of its late bearing habit. Certain of the clonal rootstocks have been shown to overcome this difficulty and future plantings will be on the growth-controlling stocks.

## Literature Cited

1. Bailey, L.H. 1922. The apple tree. MacMillan, New York. 117 p.
2. Beach, S.A. 1905. The apples of New York, Vol. I. J.B. Lyons Co., Albany, N.Y. 409 p.
3. Beach, S.A. 1905. The apples of New York, Vol. II. J.B. Lyons Co., Albany, N.Y. 360 p.

\*The concluding paragraph is by Walter Mellenthin of Hood River, Oregon.

4. Taylor,W.A. 1897. *In* Yearbook, U.S. Dep. Agr., Washington, D.C.
5. U.S. Department of Agriculture. 1915. Yearbook U.S. Dep. Agr., Washington, D.C.
6. U.S. Department of Agriculture, New England Crop Reporting Service, Mimeo Rep., Dec., 1964

# III. TRENDS IN CURRENT APPLE VARIETIES

## EMERY C. WILCOX

United States Department of Agriculture
Seattle, Washington [1]

## UNITED STATES [2]

DELICIOUS APPLES—RED AND STANDARD—NORMALLY ACcount for 25–30% of all the apples produced in the United States. In the four-year period, 1966–69, Delicious contributed about 28% of the nation's apple crop. Golden Delicious and McIntosh were virtually tied for second, with 11.7 and 11.4% respectively in the years, 1966–69. During the early part of the decade of the 1960's, McIntosh was second by a substantial amount. The average Rome Beauty crop in the four-year period, 1966–69, placed that variety in fourth place with 7.8%. Jonathan ranked fifth with 6.5%.

Other major varieties in order of importance are: York Imperial, Winesap, Stayman, Yellow Newtown and Cortland. However, the average production of these five varieties combined (18.9%) was less than Delicious production during that same period and it was significantly less than in the years, 1961–66. Minor varieties for which the United States Department of Agriculture prepares estimates are Gravenstein, Grimes Golden, Wealthy, Baldwin, Ben Davis, Black Twig, Northern Spy and Rhode Island Greening.

In the years that have elapsed since variety estimates began in 1942, apple production has tended to become more and more concentrated in winter varieties and especially Delicious, Golden Delicious and Rome. That this trend has been continu-

[1] Statistical data related to this chapter are available from American Pomological Society.

[2] Apple variety estimates prepared by the United States Department of Agriculture begin with the year 1942. These estimates are for the counties designated after each quinquennial Census of Agriculture as having "commercial production" in sufficient quantity to justify the estimate.

ing is evident from average production data for the six years, 1960–65, and for the four years, 1966–69.

*Summer Apples.* Only one summer apple variety is estimated— the Gravenstein. It rates as one of the nation's minor apple crops. Other summer varieties are grown, but the estimates are published as a group. In the years, 1942–47, summer apples contributed 5.7% of the nation's apple crop, but this class accounted for only 3.6% of the 1966–69 production. This represents a drop of about 15%. There was little change in the relative importance of summer apples during the 1960's inasmuch as this group contributed 3.7% of the United States apple crop during the period, 1960–65.

*Fall Apples.* Three apple varieties are estimated separately in the fall group. They are Grimes Golden, Jonathan and Wealthy. A miscellaneous category accounts for a small part of all fall apple crops. The fall group supplied 13.9% of the apples produced in the nation in the years, 1942–47, but only 9.9% in the period, 1960–65, and 8.7% in the years, 1966–69.

*Winter Apples.* Fourteen of the apple varieties estimated in the United States are classed as winter apples. This group includes nine of the ten most important varieties. It is not surprising, therefore, to learn that winter apples have increased in relative importance. During the early years of variety estimates, winter apples contributed 80.4% of the United States crop. By the years, 1960–65, it became 86.4% and for the period, 1966–69, 87.7%.

## INDIVIDUAL VARIETIES.

Over the years, the production of individual apple varieties has varied greatly in response to weather conditions and the tendency of apple trees, under certain conditions, to bear heavy crops one year and a lighter crop the following year. However, over the 28 years from 1942 through 1969, there were significant changes in the relative importance of individual apple varieties.

*Delicious.* Red Delicious was the leading variety in 1942 with 16.9% of the nation's apple crop. For the years, 1942–47, this variety accounted for 19.9% of the production but ranged from 16.8 in 1943 to 25.7% in 1945. In the 14 years, 1945–58, there were only two years when Delicious accounted for less than 20% of the United States total. These two were 1951 when the production dropped to 16,897,000 bushels—15.1% of that year's crop—and 1956 when the 19,277,000 bushels represented 19.0% of the total. Largest production years during the period, 1942–58 inclusive, were 1957 when 28,756,000 bushels were produced and 1958 when the estimate was 28, 737,000 bushels.

In the 11 years, 1959 through 1969, there was only one year in which Delicious production ran less than 20% of the national crop and there were eight years when it ran over 25% of the total. Low for the period was 1,116.3 million pounds* in 1960. A record high was set in 1969 when the Delicious crop was estimated at 2,065.4 million pounds—just over 30% of the total commercial crop.

Although, the state of Washington has dominated in Delicious apple production in the past 27 years of record, this variety is important in every apple producing area and in almost every apple producing state. Generally, the first five states in production are the same but the relative importance may vary from year to year. In 1969 Washington and California accounted for 58% of all Delicious apples produced in the United States. Adding Oregon gave the West Coast 61% of the Delicious crop. One of the interesting features in the history of production of this variety has been the rise of California.

Michigan, an East North Central state, generally ranks

*Beginning in 1959 U. S. production figures were changed from bushels to pounds. One bushel 42 pounds.

among the top five states and in 1969 was tied for third with Virginia, a South Atlantic state. New York, a Middle Atlantic state, has always been among the leaders in Delicious production and Pennsylvania, also a Middle Atlantic state, has been in the top five in past years.

*Golden Delicious.* Golden Delicious took over second place from McIntosh in the years, 1966–69, primarily because of the record production in 1969. In 1942, only 2,298,000 bushels were produced which was 1.8% of the nation's crop—fourteenth among the apple varieties in the United States. For the years, 1942–47, Goldens accounted for only 2.3% of the national apple crop, eleventh in rank.

Actually there was not too much change in the relative position of the Golden Delicious crop in the years, 1943–50. The crop ranged from 2.0 to 3.0% of the total apple crop and in 1950, Goldens still ranked eleventh among the 18 leading varieties. Goldens accounted for 3.1 to 3.6% in the years, 1951–55, moved to over 4.0% in 1956 and 1957, and up to 5.2% in 1958. That year (1958) the Golden Delicious crop was up to sixth nationally. In 1960 and 1961 Goldens moved to over 6% of the nation's apple crop, to 7% in 1962, to 8% in 1963 and 1964, and to 9.3% in 1965. In ranking, the Golden Delicious crop went to third place in 1963 and held that place until 1969 when it surpassed McIntosh.

The average production of Golden Delicious in the years, 1966–69, was about 670 million pounds. However, the individual years and the percentage of the nation's crop were as follows:

| Year | Million pounds | Percent |
|------|----------------|---------|
| 1966 | 595.8 | 10 |
| 1967 | 636.5 | 12 |
| 1968 | 631.5 | 12 |
| 1969 | 878.0 | 13 |

It is difficult to discuss Golden Delicious production trends by area in terms of single-year production data because of the marked alternate bearing characteristics of this variety. Nevertheless there are certain area characteristics which stand out when considering just the years 1942, 1952, 1962 and 1969.

1. This was a relatively new variety in 1942 and no one area really dominated production.
2. Washington now is the principal state by a wide margin. In 1942 this state produced 18% of all the Golden Delicious harvested in the United States. This advanced to 22% in 1952, 31% in 1962 and to 43% in 1969.
3. Virginia and Pennsylvania have always been important factors in Golden Delicious production.
4. Illinois, once in second place, has been declining in relative importance.

*McIntosh.* Like Delicious, McIntosh is more important today than in earlier years. It was the third most important variety in 1943, second in 1966 and third in 1969. The average for the six years, 1942–47, was 8.5%, but there was a very small crop in 1945, and 1946 also was well below average. From 1949 through 1966, there was only one year in which McIntosh accounted for less than 10% of the nation's apple crop. That one exception was 1952 when only 8,010,000 bushels were produced which was 8.5% of the total for that year. McIntosh moved into second place in national tonnage in 1949 and held second place (except in 1952) until 1969.

During the years, 1949–58 inclusive, the largest production in the United States was in 1958, a total of 17,188,000 bushels which was 13.5% of the total crop. Percentagewise, during those years, the high was in 1955, (14.4%), but the production that year was only 15,333,000 bushels. Over the years, McIntosh ranged from 11.4 to 14.6% of the total apple crop and in production from 610.1 million pounds in 1960 to 832.9 million pounds in 1961.

McIntosh apple production is confined largely to the Middle Atlantic, New England, and East North Central States. It is one of the few apple varieties with no western state among the five leading producers. New York has always been the dominant state with New England states second and Michigan third. In 1942 these three areas harvested 89% of all the McIntosh apples picked in the nation and in 1969 they accounted for 91%. Pennsylvania was among the top five in the years, 1942, 1952, 1962, and 1969; Wisconsin was among the leaders in 1952, 1962, and 1969.

*Rome Beauty.* Rome production increased over the years, especially after the introduction of the newer red strains. Average production for the six years, 1942–47, was 6,159,000 bushels which was 5.8% of the national apple crop during that period. Rome then ranked fifth among the 18 leading varieties grown in the United States. For the six years, 1960–65, Rome production was 7.5% of the nation's crop and Rome moved into fourth place ahead of Jonathan. In the years, 1942–58, the Rome crop usually accounted for 6.0–6.9% of the U. S. crop. Ten times in those 17 years, Rome fell within those limits. Four times, Rome accounted for less than 6.0% and three times ran 7.0% or over.

Production of Rome Beauty apples increased during the years, 1966–69, and the average for the period was 460.6 million pounds. During that period, Rome accounted for 7.8% of the nation's apple crop and held fourth place among the varieties. Record production of 534.2 million pounds was recorded in 1969.

The Rome Beauty is one of the apple varieties grown in every important apple-producing area in the United States. No one state accounted for as much as one-third of the Rome Beauty total in 1942 and in 1952, 1962 and 1969 the leading state contributed less than 20% of the total crop. In 1942 the three leading states, Washington, Ohio and Pennsylvania, had 50% of the Rome Beauty apples and in 1969 the three leaders had 41% of the total.

*Jonathan.* Jonathan is the only non-winter apple among the 10 leading varieties produced in the United States. During the period, 1942–47, Jonathan accounted for 7.4% of the U. S. crop; and in the six years, 1960–65, it accounted for 6.8%. In the first six-year period, Jonathan ranked fourth among the 18 leading varieties and it has been in fifth position the last ten years. Peak production during the years, 1942–58 inclusive, was the 10,-231,000 bushels produced in 1949. The low was 4,887,000 bushels harvested in 1945. From a percentage standpoint, the high was 7.6 in 1942 and 1949 and the low was 5.8 in 1950.

During the last 11 years, 1959–69, the high was 447.7 million pounds harvested in 1965 and the high percentage was 7.3 in 1959. Lows were 218.6 million pounds in 1960 and 6.2% in 1967. For the years, 1966–69, average production was 381.6 million pounds ranging from 327.0 million to 435.4 million pounds. The 1966–69 average for Jonathan production represented 6.5% of the United States crop. Despite the decline in percentage of total crop, the average production in the years, 1966–69, was almost twice as much as in the years, 1942–47.

Michigan has dominated Jonathan production in the United States since 1952 and has become relatively more important in recent years. In 1942 three North Central states—Michigan, Illinois and Ohio—accounted for 33% of the Jonathan production and in 1969 Michigan and Illinois together contributed 46%.

*York Imperial.* Production of York Imperial has increased about 10% over the years despite a decline in relative importance. During the six years, 1942–47, York accounted for 5.3% of the apple crop and ranked seventh in importance among the 18 major varieites. York Imperial production, 1960–65, accounted for 5.3% of the nation's apples and the rank was still seventh. Peak production came in 1942 when 8,500,000 bushels were picked, 6.7% of the U. S. crop. York Imperial tonnage dropped off sharply in 1966.

From 1960 through 1965, the average was 304.4 million pounds per year; but in 1966 the crop totaled only 199.3 million pounds, 3.5% of the total apple crop. Production picked up sharply after 1966, making the 1966–69 average 279.1 million pounds, enough to put York Imperial in sixth place among the nation's varieties. York production was greater than that of Winesap in 1947, 1968 and 1969. For the four years, 1966–69, York Imperial contributed 4.8% of the nation's apple crop.

The York Imperial apple is decidedly an eastern apple. Production has always been concentrated primarily in the adjoining states of Pennsylvania, West Virginia, Maryland and Virginia. In 1942 these states had 96% of the national York production; in 1952, 98%; in 1962, 98%; and in 1969, 100%. Normally, Virginia leads all states, but in 1969 Pennsylvania's crops was up substantially over 1968, whereas, the Virginia crop was smaller.

*Winesap.* Winesap production dropped off drastically in the years 1942–69. In 1942, Winesap was the third most important apple variety in the United States, and in the years 1943–48, ranked second. It dropped to third place in 1949, and, except for 1952 when it placed second, held third place until 1961. In succeeding years, Winesap production ranked as follows: 1961, fourth; 1962, fifth; 1963, fourth; 1964, sixth; 1965, eighth; 1966, sixth and from 1967 through 1969, seventh. For the period, 1942–47, Winesap production averaged 11.3% of the total commercial apple crop, whereas, in the 1960–65 period, the average was 6.4%. There was a drop of almost 37% in production over the years, 1942–66.

There were several years in the period, 1942–58, when Winesap production exceeded 10,000,000 bushels, and the all-time high came in 1944 with 13,892,000 bushels which represented 11.5% of the nation's apples. A smaller crop in 1945 accounted for 15.4% of the U. S. apple crop. The Winesap crop in the years, 1966–69, averaged only 272.4 million pounds. Production dropped almost steadily during those four years. The low of 258.9 million pounds was only 3.8% of the national crop. York Imperial production exceeded Winesap production in 1967, 1968, and 1969 and Winesap was down to 4.6% for the years, 1966–69.

Washington normally produces about three-quarters of all the Winesap apples grown in the United States. Virginia is the second-ranking state by a wide margin over the third place state. The two leaders had 90% of the 1942 crop, 90% of the 1952 crop, 89% of the 1962 crop and 88% of the 1969 crop. Colorado and West Virginia have always been among the five leaders in Winesap production, and in recent years, California has moved into the top five.

*Stayman.* Stayman production in the years, 1966–69, averaged only 228.8 million pounds, but this was enough to keep this variety in eighth place. The average represented only 3.9% of the nation's crop compared with 5.3% for the years, 1960–65. Stayman constituted 5.2% of the national commercial crop (1942–47) and ranked sixth among apple varieties. More Stayman apples were harvested in 1942 than in any other year since varietal estimates were made. It is a crop, however, which has been subject to considerable year-to-year variation.

Stayman apple production is concentrated primarily in Pennsylvania, Virginia and West Virginia, but North Carolina and New Jersey also are important producers. In 1942 Pennsylvania and Virginia accounted for 54% of the United States Stayman crop and in 1969 these same two states had 48% of the total. West Virginia has generally been fourth in Stayman production and has usually contributed about 9% of the crop. North Carolina came into the 1952 rating in third place with about 10% of that year's crop. This state ranked fourth in 1962 but was back to third in 1969. New Jersey replaced Ohio in fifth place in 1962 and 1969.

*Yellow Newtown.* The ninth ranking variety in the years, 1966–69, was the Yellow Newtown with 3.1% of the United States commercial production. During the years, 1942–47, Newtown

accounted for 4.3% of the national total and in the early period
of variety estimates, Yellow Newtown was eighth in importance. Production was uniform in the years, 1942–58, running
between 4,000,000 and 5,000,000 bushels in 12 of those 17
years. Four times, the production was between 3,300,000 and
4,000,000 and one time exceeded 5,000,000 bushels. Following
1959, there were only two years in which production exceeded
200 million pounds. Average production of Yellow Newtown in
the years, 1966–69, was 182.1 million pounds with a range of
168.0 million to 204.1 million pounds.

Yellow Newtown production has always been concentrated
in California and Oregon. The commercial crop of Yellow Newtown was estimated in only four states in 1942. The above two
West Coast states in 1942 had 76% of the nation's crop of
Newtown and Virginia and Washington had the rest. The Cali-
fornia-Oregon combination had 90% of the Newtown crop in
1952 and 95% in 1962. Commercial estimates of Newtown were
made only in California and Oregon in 1969.

*Cortland.* Ranked tenth among the leading varieties produced
in the United States is Cortland. In the four-year period, 1966–
69, the average production was 143.9 million pounds compared
with 151.6 million pounds during the six-years, 1960–65; and,
Cortland accounted for 2.5% of the nation's apple crop in the
1966–69 period against 2.6% in the 1960–65 period. In the
years, 1942–47, production was considerably less and this variety accounted for only 1.3% of the total apple crop in the United
States and ranked seventeenth in importance. The all-time high
of 162.6 million pounds came in 1969, exceeding the previous
record of 161.5 million pounds in 1960. Northern Spy and
Rhode Island Greening were close behind.

Middle Atlantic and New England states have always been
the primary producers of Cortland apples. Indeed, in 1942 New
York and Pennsylvania accounted for 82% of the Cortland crop
and New England contributed the remainder. The 1952 Cortland crop was 75% from New York and Pennsylvania and 13%

from New England. Ohio and California were the other important producers that year.

New York and Pennsylvania accounted for 65% of the 1962
Cortland crop with New England contributing 17%. Michigan
moved into third place in 1962 and Ohio was fifth. Again in
1969, New York and Pennsylvania harvested 65% of the Cortland crop. New England had about the same percentage of the
total as in 1962 and Michigan had the same. Wisconsin appeared in fifth place supplanting Ohio.

*Minor Varieties.* Most minor varieties of apples grown in the
United States showed sharp changes in relative importance over
the 29 years, 1942–69. Two varieties—Northern Spy and
Rhode Island Greening—show substantial increases. Gravenstein, Baldwin, Grimes Golden, Ben Davis and Black Twig
dropped off sharply.

*Percent of U.S. Commercial Apple Crop*

| Variety | 1942-47 | 1960-65 | 1966-69 |
|---|---|---|---|
| Northern Spy | 1.7 | 2.3 | 2.3 |
| Rhode Island Greening | 1.9 | 2.3 | 2.3 |
| Gravenstein | 2.7 | 1.9 | 2.0 |
| Baldwin | 3.4 | 1.6 | 1.1 |
| Wealthy | | | 0.7 |
| Grimes Golden | 2.1 | 0.8 | 0.4 |
| Ben Davis | 2.2 | 0.8 | 0.4 |
| Black Twig | 0.8 | 0.2 | — |

Four of the seven minor varieties of apples for which estimates
were made in 1969 were grown primarily in the Middle Atlantic
and New England states. In that year New York was the leading
producer of Wealthy, Rhode Island Greening, Baldwin and Ben
Davis apples. New England ranked second in Gravenstein and
Baldwin production in 1969 and was third in the production of

Northern Spy and Rhode Island Greening. Michigan was the leading producer of Northern Spy apples in 1969 with New York second and New England third. California was the leader in Gravenstein production with New England the only other area for which there were estimates. Indiana produced more Grimes Golden in 1969 than any other state, but West Virginia normally is the leader. Actually the positions of the leading states in 1969 were not greatly different than in 1942. New York was then the leader in the production of the same four—Wealthy, Rhode Island Greening, Baldwin and Ben Davis. Michigan led all states in Northern Spy, California led in Gravenstein, West Virginia was the primary producer of Grimes Golden and Virginia led in Black Twig production.

## CANADA

Canadian statistics on apple varieties are not continuous. However, data are available for the years, 1949–51 (an average), and for the individual years 1961, 1966 and 1969 from the Fruit Division, C.D.A. Provincial Census.

Production figures show that three varieties dominate. These are the McIntosh, Delicious and Northern Spy. Average production of these three during the three years, 1949–51, amounted to about 9,549,000 bushels (45 lb.) out of a total crop of 19,100,000 bushels or roughly 50%. The production of the same three varieties in 1969 was 16,564,000 bushels which was almost 72% of the 23,168,000-bushel Canadian apple crop.

Cortland ranked fourth in production in 1969 and Winesap was fifth with 3.3 and 2.7% respectively. No other variety contributed as much as 2.0% of the total apple crop in 1969, although there were several varieties which accounted for 1.0–1.9%.

Canada has many apple varieties which are produced in small quantities. This is demonstrated by the fact that the 1949–51 average figures showed 27.7% in "others," none of which individually was as important as the Melba which, at that time, accounted for no more than 1.2% of the country's apples. In

1961 the "other" classification covered 17.0% of the apple crop, in 1966 it was 11.1% and in 1969 this group constituted 10.8% of the entire Canadian apple crop.

For this reason, it is not possible to make seasonal group comparisons i.e.—Summer, Fall and Winter. Nevertheless, the data do cover the major and significant varieties of Canadian apples.

*McIntosh.* McIntosh is Canada's most popular apple variety. Average production for the 3 years, 1949–51, was 5,597,000 bushels which was 29.3% of the Canadian apple crop. By 1961, the McIntosh crop had climbed to 6,426,000 bushels and production continued upward to 8,552,000 bushels in 1966 when this variety produced 41.4% of the total. Production continued to increase. In 1969 the preliminary indication was 11,163,000 bushels of McIntosh apples and this represented 48.2% of Canada's apples.

*Delicious.* Variability in production data make it difficult to establish a trend in Delicious apple production in Canada. Figures for the 1949–51 period show 2,915,000 bushels which represented 15.3% of the average Canadian crop in those years. Production was down to 2,057,000 bushels in 1961 which was 12.5% of the crop. In 1966 the Delicious crop was estimated at 3,335,000 bushels—16.3% of the total crop. In 1969 production was 3,228,000 bushels and this was 13.9% of all the apples produced.

*Northern Spy.* Ranked third among Canadian apples is Northern Spy or Spy. Each year of record showed a greater production than the previous period—starting with 1,037,000 bushels average (1949–51) to 2,173,000 bushels in 1969. There has been also an increase in relative importance. In the 1949–51 period the Northern Spy accounted for 5.4% of the Canadian apple crop, but in 1969 it contributed 9.4%.

*Winesap.* Winesap statistics show the same type of production variation as Delicious. Average production in the three years, 1949–51, was 843,000 bushels. The amount harvested was

714,000 bushels in 1961, 1,134,000 bushels in 1966 and only
633,000 bushels in 1969. Percent of total Canadian apples was
as follows:

| | | | |
|---|---|---|---|
| 1949–51 | 4.4% | 1966 | 5.5% |
| 1961 | 4.3% | 1969 | 2.7% |

*Cortland.* The Cortland variety actually ranked fourth in 1969,
ahead of Winesap, with 755,000 bushels or 3.3% of the total
apple crop. However, the sharp variations in Winesap production make comparisons as close as 3.3 and 2.7% open to question. The available Cortland data do show an upward trend.
Production started with 374,000 bushels (1949–51) and rose to
541,000 to 563,000 and finally to 755,000 bushels. Percent of
total crop started at 2.0 and ended at 3.3.

*Minor Varieties.* As already noted, there are many minor varieties grown in Canada. Estimates are available for only a few. In
some cases there are no estimates for each of the four periods
for which estimates were made, indicating that some minor
varieties were placed in the "other" classification one year and
not in another.

| *Variety* | *Percent of total apple crop, 1969* |
|---|---|
| Spartan | 1.6 |
| Lobo | 1.6 |
| Gravenstein | 1.5 |
| Fameuse | 1.1 |
| Wagener | 1.0 |
| Rhode Island Greening | 1.0 |
| King | .9 |
| Yellow Newtown | .8 |
| Russet | .7 |
| Rome Beauty | .4 |

# IV. DELICIOUS

## VIRGINIA MAAS*

Tacoma, Washington

STARTING AS A SMALL INSIGNIFICANT SEEDLING IN JESSE Hiatt's Peru, Iowa orchard, about 1870, the original Delicious tree was not welcomed or heralded as the beginning of an apple that in time would be said to represent the crowning point of achievement in the origination of American varieties. On the contrary, Mr. Hiatt twice unceremoniously cut down the young tree because it was not in the row.

With an urge to fulfill its destiny, this hardy child pushed its way into the world again, larger than before. And Jesse, a man of patience and persistence himself, with a natural sympathy for anything that could withstand adversity, felt compassion for this struggling, youngster.

"If thee must live, thee may," the Quaker said, trimming some of the branches, and cutting off the top to encourage growth and proper form.

Because the sturdy sprout was growing near an old Yellow Bellflower tree, Hiatt surmised that the latter might be one of the parents, and he wondered what kind of fruit the seedling would bear. He had always enjoyed experimenting and had made a practice of grafting several varieties on one tree. He had two very good apple varieties of his own, the Hiatt Sweet and the Hiatt Black.

The Bellflower fruit was attractive, of good quality, with a peculiar long pointed shape terminating in five points at the blossom end. Because of these unusual characteristics he was convinced that any offspring of the Bellflower would surely produce fruit with similar attributes.

For the next several years he carefully tended and cared for

*Mrs. Maas is a free lance writer who, at the request of W.A. Luce, wrote this chapter. Material was obtained from various sources including Stark Nurseries, E.C. Blodgett, M.D. Aichele, and W.A. Luce.

the tree. When the tree was 10 years old, Jesse was delighted to discover his new tree was boasting a blossom cluster. By harvest time there was one apple which had hung tenaciously to the limb until maturity. Jesse admired the beautiful flashing strawberry color streaked with lines of darker red. He was now certain that this seedling was a progeny of the old Bellflower tree for, even though the color differed for this new apple it had the same unusual shape, and the five points on the end were even more prominent than those on the Bellflower fruit. Taking out his pocket knife he carefully pared the one and only apple. What would it taste like? In great excitement, Jesse told his wife, "Ma, this is the best apple in the whole world!" He never changed his mind.

Years later many people expressed the same opinion, including A.J. Mason, former President of the Hood River, Oregon Apple Growers' Union who said, "It is the best flavored apple I have ever tasted." E.P. Powell, a veteran fruit grower in many parts of the United States from New York to Florida, and the author of *The Orchard and Fruit Garden*, said "It is most prominent, for both beauty and quality, for its bearing capacity, and its ability to win the favor of cook as well as prince. All hail Delicious, noblest apple in the world today!"

One would think that an apple which later proved to be so truly delightful to the eye and palate would have gained instant acclaim, but the life of the Delicious from the start hung virtually by a thread. What if the seedling, after being cut down, had not sprouted the third time? If Jesse Hiatt had not been prompted by sympathy to allow the seedling a place in his orchard, the Delicious apple would have remained unknown.

Getting a safe spot to spread its roots was only one of the necessary factors for the success of Delicious seedling, and even though Jesse made this possible, there were still the hazards of weather to face. When the tree trunk was six inches in diameter, the top was blown to the northeast, leaving the body exposed to sun and wind. It became affected by sunscald, the bark cracked and began to peel off. Determined to save his tree, which he now called the Hawkeye, Hiatt fastened a heavy cover about the body, and kept it on for many years.

However, the destiny of the apple fit for the Gods still tottered precariously in their laps. There was no doubt in Jesse's mind that his Hawkeye with its superb flavor and good characteristics was indeed the best in the world. But how could he convince the people? He sent exhibits of his apple to the Iowa fairs, but they were scarcely noticed. Established varieties took the blue ribbons.

When he tried to persuade his friend, Judge W. H. Lewis, a nurseryman of nearby Winterset, that it would be profitable for him to graft and sell the trees, the nurseryman failed to see any future in Hiatt's apple.

Jesse carried his apples wherever he went in an effort to bring the fruit into public focus, but this availed him nothing but a remark from the *Winterset News* publisher to the effect that Jesse was batty and the apple no good. By this time many persons would have been ready to give up and the world would never have known the apple which in later years was said by Luther Burbank to be "the best in quality of any apple which I have so far tested."

But undaunted after 11 years of promotion, and still convinced that he had the world's best apple, Hiatt sent four apples in 1893 to a fruit show being held in Louisiana, Mo. This show was sponsored by Stark Nurseries and exhibits of new fruits from all over America and abroad were invited. Prizes were offered for the best, promising, high quality, heavy producing fruits. Here, at last the Hawkeye was to receive attention. When the judges beheld the plate of beautiful, long shaped, highly flavored fruit with their five distinctive points at one end, only first place was good enough for such an apple.

Taking his first bite of the apple to judge its quality, C. M. Stark, President of Stark Nurseries, exclaimed, "My that's *Delicious*—and that's the name for it."* Mr. Stark habitually carried

*For more detail on the introduction of the Delicious variety, see *The Stark Story* in Sept. 1966 Bulletin of the Missouri Historical Society.

a little red book in his pocket in which he jotted down appropri-
ate names for new fruit varieties as they occurred to him. For
years he had retained the name Delicious for a fruit worthy of
the superb title, and here was the apple for which he had been
waiting. Where had it come from, and who was the exhibitor?
No one could furnish the answers. In the confusion of the show,
the name and address of the sender had been lost. Fate had dealt
another blow to Jesse Hiatt's hopes for recognition of his Hawkeye.

But luckily for the apple lovers of the world, this old Quaker
had early learned the importance of patience and persistence,
and he awaited another opportunity to exhibit the apple of his
eye. The wheel of fortune was turning, and in Missouri Mr.
Stark, having recognized in this winner a potential to revolu-
tionize the apple industry, decided to repeat the Apple Show
and Fruit Fair the following year with the hope that the owner
of this magnificent fruit would enter it again.

As opening day for the 1894 Show approached, the interested
parties eagerly opened and examined each entry as it arrived,
searching for the fabulous apple from the unknown exhibitor.
At last on the very day the Fair opened, a barrel was received
which bore a return tag addressed to Jesse Hiatt, Peru, Iowa.
The barrel top was quickly removed, exposing the beautiful
apples with their streaked strawberry colors, the precious fruit
which Hiatt had refused to allow to remain insignificant and
unknown.

To such a tenuous thread of circumstance and chance, the
Delicious clung and won its right to be called the greatest
red apple of the world, the forerunner of a major segment, as
well as the backbone, of the vast apple industry of America
today.

Excitedly Stark wrote to Hiatt to learn more about the apple
and the history of the tree. In answer Jesse wrote, in part, "I am
nearly 70 years old and have raised apples all my life and would
not willingly overestimate this apple for 40 such varieties, but
if it is not a better apple than any in your long list, it will cost

you nothing. I have never seen a man taste it but who says it is the best apple he ever saw. It hangs on the tree as well as Ben Davis, keeps as well, is a good shipper, is as large, of finer color. The tree is as strong a grower and very hardy. It bears young and bears every year. Once you introduce it, there will be little call for Jonathan. The tree is similar to Winesap, except branches are stronger and need little or no pruning. Both tree and fruit are perfect models. The tree is strong, has finely molded limbs, which are adapted to bearing great weights of fruit. It does not succumb to blight and never shows any signs of tenderness. During the last eight years, drought and cold have killed three-fifths of my orchard up here in Iowa, but this tree has withstood it all. It is praised by all who have tasted it, and it has a peculiar quality which cannot be surpassed or described and has a delicious fragrance. It is brilliant red in color, often mingled with gold near the blossom end. All declare it to be the best apple in the world."

After correspondence with Jesse, Stark boarded a train for Peru, Iowa to personally inspect the tree which was now so very important. He found that it possessed the necessary attributes, and he purchased the propagating rights.

Not wishing to wait the usual length of time required to introduce a new variety to the public, the Starks sent as gifts a few Delicious trees with each order being sent all over the country, gambling on the chance that they would produce in different regions. The gamble paid off, and in a few years they were flooded by letters from people in all parts of the country asking the name of the apple which tasted like no other they had eaten, and requesting more trees to plant.

The adaptability of the Delicious to grow in a variety of climates caused Richard Dalton, President of the Missouri State Board of Horticulture to say that it "may be profitably grown in any climate where the apple is at all at home." For 40 years a successful, progressive, practical fruit grower, whose unceasing efforts toward the betterment of horticulture have been of inestimable value to the orchardists of the land, Dalton went on to say, "My belief is the experience of a few years to come will establish the greater worth of this wonderful apple, and instead of giving our time and expending vast money and labor to growing inferior varieties of apples, we will turn our attention to the production of the Delicious and give to the world the delight of a fruit acceptable to the universal taste. The propagation of the Delicious will inspire the apple grower to expend his energy and time in the production of a fruit that meets with the world's tastes and wants."

The first commercial display of Delicious was at a horticultural congress at Council Bluffs, Iowa. One hundred bushels were sliced for samples and given to visitors and growers.

So convinced were Stark Nurseries that the Delicious was indeed the King of the apple family that they spent three-quarters of a million dollars to introduce it to the world, and in a quarter of a century they sent out nearly eight million trees. The annual value of the Delicious apple crop by 1922 was estimated at 12 million dollars.

To commemorate the original Delicious apple tree, which had become such an important factor in the apple industry, a six-thousand pound boulder monument was placed in beautiful Winterset Park, Winterset, Iowa and inscribed with the following words:

To commemorate the Discovery in Madison County, Iowa of a Variety of Apple by Jesse Hiatt, A.D. 1872 and Called by Him "The Hawkeye". Sole Right to Propagate Acquired by C. M. Stark, A.D. 1894. Introduced and Disseminated Throughout the Apple World as the Delicious Apple. Erected A.D. 1922, Iowa State Horticultural Society, Madison County Historical Society, Historical Department of Iowa.

The dedication ceremony which was held in the park in Winterset Aug. 15, 1922, proved to be one of the most notable gatherings that ever attended a similar event in that state. National leaders in Horticulture, Pomology, and the Publishing

Field, along with thousands of people from Madison and the surrounding counties, joined in the celebration. Among the dignitaries was Professor C. I. Lewis, Managing Editor of the American Fruit Grower and former director of the Oregon Agricultural Experiment Station. In his address entitled *The Delicious Apple, its Place in American Pomology* he said, in part:

"The Delicious apple represents the crowning point of achievement in the origination of American varieties. No variety has been originated which is superior to the Delicious in quality; few can equal it in production. The high yielding varieties like Delicious, Jonathan, Winesap, and Stayman which tend to produce annually big crops are the varieties which are making fruit growing profitable in the West. No variety of apple of American origin ever had quicker distribution than the Delicious and none was ever accepted more readily by the American public. It is one of the best known varieties which we have, and rightly so, for its large size, its beautiful color, its delicious aroma and quality. In the origination of the Delicious, a high standard has been set for us in the development of future varieties. Gradually some of the older varieties are slipping by the wayside; the Baldwin has probably passed its zenith, being an irregular bearer, winter killing frequently and being subject to Baldwin Spot, which has contributed to restricting its planting. The future is going to demand fruits, coupled with productiveness, vigor and good appearance. We see, through all the ages, man has gone through all sorts of hardship and privation to carry fruit with him to the end of the earth. As a result, some races, especially in the tropics, subsist on fruit alone. Can we not, with the later generation, show that same zeal in the improvement of our varieties and the origination of new ones? What more can we do for posterity than to bring forth beautiful, superior fruits, nuts, flowers and vegetables?"

Fourteen years later, in 1936, when Hiatt's tree was 56 years old, W. B. Landis, then owner of the Hiatt Farm wrote the following: "I wanted you to know that the original Delicious tree remains in healthy, vigorous condition and that I am taking the best possible care of it. It had a dandy crop last fall and prospects for another this year are bright."

But previous to all this, back in the year 1898 Jesse Hiatt's "Hawkeye" was still unrecognized, and Jesse died oblivious of what his patience and perseverance had done for the world. His death was unnoticed by the State Horticultural Society, and no mention of his great service to the apple industry was noted in his obituary. It is doubtful if his ears ever heard the words that would have meant so much to him, the words Clarence Stark spoke when he returned from his trip to Iowa to investigate the history of the tree, "This is the apple of my dreams. My search for the perfect apple is over. It is going to create a great sensation, and I have outlined in my mind future plans for propagation—even now I can see millions of young Delicious trees in our nursery fields ready to be sent forth to bless every fruit section of the entire world."

Hiatt could never know that years later, before 1913, one Colorado grower sold his selected exhibit of Delicious apples for $15 per bushel. Some prize winning Delicious brought as high as $25 for a single bushel box. They have been sent as special gifts to the Presidents of the United States and to the Crowned Monarchs of Europe. One Washington planter received $2,037.50 for one crop from 36 nine year old Delicious trees. Chicago's largest fruit store realized as much as $40 from a single barrel sold at retail. Delicious from all regions commanded top prices—from New Mexico, Minnesota, Virginia, North Carolina, New England.

Men have waxed poetic over this magnificent apple, and well they might. A lyrical tribute to Jesse Hiatt and his apple was given by the Honorable Frank Femmons, California's veteran horticulturist, who for the better portion of a century was in the foreground of horticultural development—a practical orchardist, a careful, keen observer, a man whose judgment of any new fruit usually proved to be correct. He said,

"No apple can compare with it. It is indeed a new creation, out from which will spring a grander type of fruit to meet the developed taste and requirements of the world. It has but one limitation—for years to come, as it becomes better known, our orchards will fail to grow enough to meet the world's demand. Jesse Hiatt, in growing that original tree of Delicious, reared to himself a living monument that is fast spreading its branches over the apple loving world. Its bending boughs of beauty, like a benediction, will give a new delight to all nations and people. Its fruit will be a joy and satisfaction to generations yet unborn. No earthly hero of war and conquest ever bequeathed such rich inheritance to the world. His name and the benefit he conferred upon mankind should be engraved, not only on the memory of time, but chiseled on an enduring pedestal beside the old parent tree that grew from out of his loving care."

On Armistice Day of November 1940, a record subzero storm raged through Iowa killing most of the orchards, and reportedly killing the original Delicious tree. Word of the disaster spread rapidly. At Stark Nurseries in Missouri, the death was deeply mourned by all. Various newspapers published tearful obituaries; one radio commentor, Fulton Lewis Jr., utilized one entire evening's radio time giving a fitting farewell eulogy to this "Mother of Millions of Trees." But still true to its indomitable spirit, this weathered pioneer refused to pass into oblivion. Staging a dramatic, almost impossible comeback, it pushed up two new sprouts from its roots and in several years began bearing annual crops again. This was possible because the tree was a seedling with top and root being nothing but Delicious, not a graft on a seedling root. These trees were still standing in 1965, enclosed by a fence that protects them from farm stock.

The hardiness of the Delicious was proved in the northern part of the United States by the man who put Minnesota on the Horticultural map, Harold Simmons, a recognized and honored authority. His orchard of Delicious was one of the first to demonstrate that variety's great value for the northern areas because of its resistance to extreme weather conditions. According to Simmons, "One season in particular is demonstrative of what the Delicious trees have been subjected to as a supreme test. The winter of 1911–12 was the coldest, most severe winter in the history of the Weather Bureau of the state, sub-zero weather for weeks at a time, with the thermometer going as low as 47 degrees below zero. The Delicious trees came out as well and grew as well the following spring as the well-known hardy northern varieties. Delicious is a combination of quality and hardiness that cannot be surpassed."

Quotations by well known authorities praising the various characteristics and attributes of this famous apple are too numerous to list, but a few succint phrases should be brought to our attention. Silas Wilson, Idaho's great Judge of Apple Shows throughout America said "Tests proved it the best keeper of any." E. O. Taylor, formerly Horticultural Inspector and County Entomologist of Colorado said, "in quality of flesh it is unsurpassed. Delicious is par excellence—wood being of strong texture, bears heavy loads without breaking." One of Utah's foremost orchardists and horticulturists, Summer Gleason, called it the "Faultless Apple" That the Delicious is an easy tree to prune, to spray, to thin and to pick,—a profitable apple to grow, was the conviction of H. M. Magie, one of Virginia's most prominent growers. In the words of Col. G. B. Brackett, a former Pomologist of USDA, Washington, D.C., fondly known in Iowa as the "Father of Horticulture", "What more can be said of this wonderful apple than is implied in its very name, Delicious?"

These comments expressed by experienced horticulturists of the 1913 era are echoed by recognized authorities of the present day. According to W. A. Luce, retired Yakima County, Wash. tree fruit agent, former President of the American Pomological Society, and international orchard consultant, "Many growers still believe that the Standard Delicious is a better flavored apple than the new redder strains; one reason perhaps might be that the Delicious was generally left to hang on the tree longer to get color and thus gain more maturity and flavor." One of the most profound statements is that of Dr. Earle Blodgett, Plant Pathologist of Washington State Department of Agriculture, "Never before in the history of Horticulture has so large an industry been so dependent, so extensively influenced and so favorably promoted by one variety, as in the case of the Delicious Apple."

The Red Delicious apple is now the world's most popular variety and is grown on all continents. Its high color and characteristic shape make it a favorite for both grower and consumer. It seems that everyone knows the name and can recognize the five points that make it different from other varieties.

Although grown generally for fresh use, the Delicious is now used extensively as a juice apple especially in the Northwest. All fruit below Fancy Grade in Washington State, the leading Delicious area, go into a pasteurized apple juice.

The Delicious variety has been improved through selection. No other variety in the world has shown so many color mutations. Perhaps this is due in part to the millions of trees propagated and the wide area over which the variety has been grown during the past half century. There seems to be no end to the number of sports that are found from year to year. As a parent however, the Declicious has not produced potential leaders when crossed with other popular varieties.

Perhaps the weakest quality of the Delicious strains is the tendency to become mealy when ripe. To preserve crispness, it is necessary to place the fruit in cold storage immediately after removal from the tree. When picked and stored properly, theDelicious can be considered a late winter variety. It responds well to CA storage and can be kept in excellent condition until late spring, at least 6-8 months.

Maturity standards for picking Red Delicious are often set up in commercial producing areas of the U.S. Committees are appointed to determine, each season, when the fruit is considered sufficiently mature. Any harvesting of fruit ahead of the date set for any particular area must be done with the approval of local state inspectors.

Standards for maturity are based on a number of factors. The first is the number of days from full bloom—145 days being considered best. Other factors include: ground color—the change from green to yellow, flesh color—the transition from greenish to white, and, the starchiness of the flesh—generally by tasting. There is much support in some commercial areas of Washington for basing the early picking of Red Delicious on total solids tests (indicating the change from starch to sugar). Many feel that there should be a law to govern the time of picking of Red Delicious in order to avoid the shipment of immature fruit.

## STANDARD SPORTS

### Starking.

The original Delicious tree that changed the horticultural map of the world was not only the Mother of Millions of Trees, but also a mother to progeny with a potential to out do even their famous parent.

However, as wonderful as it is, there is still one detracting characteristic of the Delicious. This one fault is that in some years it takes on its beautiful high red color late in the season. In order to get the color which is necessary to obtain highest prices in the market, it was sometimes left on the tree too long and the result was overripe, mealy fruit undesirable for market. This fault was overcome by one of the most important offspring, the Starking, which was produced from a bud sport on a particular Delicious tree grown in the orchard of Mr. Lewis Mood in Monroeville, N. J. in 1921. Mood noticed that, when the tree first fruited, one limb bore apples that had colored up much earlier than those on the balance of the tree. It continued to do so each year. At picking time the apples were a deep, dark red instead of the usual light red stripe. They did not ripen any earlier, but colored earlier, thus enabling him to pick them at the right time for the longest keeping. When picked hard ripe, they kept well until late spring without becoming mealy, and because of their better and more uniform color, always sold for more money than any other apple he raised.

This amazing apple was noticed by a State Horticulturist who passed along the information to the Stark Nurseries. They immediately visited the tree, and after months of correspondence and thorough investigation, purchased it for $6,000 just to procure this one limb. They erected a cage around the tree to protect it, and then began to make a series of tests to prove that scions from that limb would produce trees yielding apples with the same early coloring, supercolor characteristics. It was found that, because it originated as a single limb, it was a true bud sport and would continue to produce the same type of fruit when propagated and grown in orchards elsewhere.

The late M.J. Dorsey, prominent horticulturist of Illinois said, "This apple is worth millions to this country's fruit growers. It is my belief that this one limb will make horticultural history. This limb is no doubt a true bud sport. It is a very, very rare occurrence in nature. Only once in millions of times do we find this and there are only a few instances where varieties have been produced in this manner. More has been done by this natural bud sport than can be done by any known cultural method."

Practically every apple on the Starking trees was extra fancy in color, a feature of extreme importance to every fruit grower.

On August 31, 1925 a group of 1500 to 2000 scientific men, representing about 20 states, gathered for a meeting in the New Jersey orchard that produced the Starking to inspect the original limb and second generation trees. Without a dissenting voice they unqualifiedly endorsed this valuable addition to the race of Delicious type apples, the outstanding horticultural acquisition of the times.

Professor S.P. Hollister, Horticulturist of Connecticut Agricultural College later said, "Pomological history was made at that meeting when Starking was publicly introduced to the world. The people who attended may never have another opportunity of being present at such a memorable meeting."

It paralleled the notable ceremony held in Iowa in 1922 to dedicate the boulder monument to the original Delicious. Delicious blazed the way, but Starking surpassed it. Following the pattern of its antecedent which changed horticultural history of that era, upholding and surpassing the qualities of its fabulous mother, the starking earned its own spectacular popularity. By passing every test that the scientific horticulturist and the thinking orchardist required, the Starking soon took its place on the list of valuable American apples and became of tremendous importance to the orchard industry.

Of this wonderful horticultural phenomenon, Luther Burbank said in 1925, "You have in Starking all the fine characteristics of the Original Delicious with the very valuable addition of earlier and deeper all-over-red color. You do not have to test its adaptability—its reputation is already made because it is simply an imporved Delicious and will grow and succeed wherever Delicious succeeds. The more brilliant solid color will bring higher prices to the fruit grower. Because the fruit colors up much sooner, it can be picked at the proper time, and will thus maintain its juicy high quality late in the season, instead of becoming mealy like the old Delicious. With the extra fancy high color that the Starking brings to the Delicious, everybody will benefit through the more attractive appearance and longer keeping qualities of Starking."

The next year on December 4, 1926 the Starking was awarded the famous Wilder Medal—the Nobel Prize of the Horticultural World presented by the American Pomological Society. The judges unanimously agreed that the Starking richly deserved this Highest Honor in the Fruit World, an honor bestowed only on fruit introductions of extraordinary merit. They were tremendously impressed by its brilliant beauty and early coloring habit, which permits earlier picking and assures longer storage.

Starking is a large apple and the Extra Fancy pack will generally run from 64 to 80 to the bushel; the color is deep dark red, with characteristic overstripe and goes all the way in to the calyx and to the stem. The skin is thick, making it one of the best shippers. Its beautiful oblong conic shape with the five points on the blossom end—as prominent as the knuckles of your clenched fist makes the apple easily recognizable in the dark.

It must be said that in the past 20 years there has been increasing evidence that some Starking orchards do not have the best fruit color characteristics, but already this fault is being corrected through the introduction of the "Frank" strain. After being tested by Stark Nurseries, this strain was eventually selected by them to take the place of the original Starking, and it is understood the latter will be displaced entirely by propagations of "Frank". It originated in the orchard of Frank Rypczyski of Hood River, Ore. who first observed it as a limb sport on a 7 year old Starking tree. It is over stripe type which colors earlier and darker than Starking.

**Richared.** Discovery of the Delicious and Starking varieties made growers more aware of the occurrence of horticultural phenomena and alerted them to constant watching for such an event. This careful observation in orchards resulted in 1926 in the finding of another offspring of the royal family of Delicious to vie for honors with its sister, the fabulous Starking. This new blush type was commercially introduced as Richared.

It originated near Monitor, Wash., about 1919 in the Delicious orchard of L. J. Richardson who noted a higher fruit color on one whole tree. He began a careful study of this tree and brought it to the attention of Columbia and Okanogan Nursery in Wenatchee, Wash. After negotiations with the nursery, a testing period began with this better colored strain. Richardson was then furnished roots for a thousand root grafts which he grew the following year for a scion orchard to provide wood for topgrafting and for nursery trees. The improved fruit color was retained in the trees propagated from the original one.

Some individuals think the flesh of Richared is finer in texture and whiter in color than the original Delicious but persons, who are very exacting in their tastes, still prefer the original Delicious. However, the average person would probably be unable to make any distinction. It colors nearly all Extra Fancy Grade, and the keeping qualities are excellent.

Though the honor came 27 years after its sister, Starking, had received the award, Richared also earned the Wilder Medal in 1953 as a very outstanding strain of Delicious (Fig. 1).

Richared became popular because of its rich blush color, and was widely planted. It has been one of the leading strains of Delicious and is well known in many foreign countries. However, in the United States, it has gracefully abdicated the throne to its daughter, Royal Red Delicious, and thus the saying, "One that follows shall be greater than the last," continues to unfold with each new discovery in the apple kingdom.

*Shotwell.* A Delicious progeny of interest, particularly from the historical standpoint, is the Shotwell which was one of the earliest improved strains to be patented. It arose in 1928 as a bud sport on a Delicious tree in the Harry Shotwell orchard in the Wenatchee Valley, Wash. The fruit colored earlier and darker than its parent, or even the Richared, and was of a stripe type. It had outstanding qualities which made it a valuable apple for commercial growing and shipping and it took its place in the apple world as an important member locally, but was not extensively planted in other areas.

Shotwell limbs join the trunk nearly at right angles, thus eliminating narrow crotches. These stronger crotches reduce the need for bracing or supports. Weak crotch is a common fault in Delicious and its other sports.

Shotwell has an established place with horticulturists because it is responsible for the bud sport Topred.

*Red King.* This variant was first observed by E. Barclay Brauns in 1936 as a limb sport on a mature Starking in the Barker Fruit

Company orchard at Riverside, Wash. The fruit colored earlier and better than Starking. Early propagations were fruited and after a few years of testing Plant Patent No. 1411 was given. Some of the early propagations were less color stable than the later selections. It is regarded as one of the major sports of Starking.

*Vance.* Vance was discovered in 1929 by R.G. Vance as a limb sport on a 10 year old Delicious tree in his orchard in Albemarle County, Va. It is a blush or solid type that colors earlier and darker than Delicious but it reverts freely to the striped type. The propagator of this apple claims that it also *matures* earlier. Planted commercially in the East, it has not found a place in the West.

*Royal Red.* J.A. Snyder and Walter Plough of Columbia and Okanogan Nursery, Wenatchee, Wash. noted a limb sport on a Richared Delicious tree in the Company orchard in 1948. The fruit colored earlier and better than that of its parent. It is predominantly a blush type, but faint striping may occur. Royal Red found good acceptance and enjoys a prominent place in the fruit world, particularly in Northwestern areas.

*Hi Early.* George W. Neff of Pateros, Wash. found about 1945 a young tree in his Starking orchard that was producing fruit that colored earlier and better than that of his other trees. It was a stripe type. The tree was used for extensive propagation as Hi Early. This was one of the earliest sports of the new era (1950) and it has maintained a leading place for many years. Currently, it is well accepted and plantings in widely separated areas have been held in high esteem.

*Chelan Red.* In 1947 J.D. Hamilton of Manson, Wash. observed a tree, then about 15 years old, that bore characteristic Delicious apples but which colored much earlier and darker than Starking. The color was a blush type and, on maturity, a very deep, dark red. In fact it has been regarded, even until now, as one of the darkest red strains. It was increased locally on a commercial scale and was awarded Patent No. 1811. While propagation of the variety was closely restricted to the original area for many years, it eventually was propagated and planted on a large scale in the Prosser area of the Yakima Valley. Here it was known, unfortunately, as the "Roza or Whitstrah Red". A sport developed in the Manson area, "Crowder", is considered identical with Chelan Red. The variety, Chelan Red, is well established commercially and, even though some people claim it is too dark, it appears to be generally well accepted.

*Red Queen.* This sport, bearing well colored stripe type fruit, was observed by Russel Myers of Consolidated Orchards of Paw Paw, W. Va. in 1952 as a limb mutation of Starking. Red Queen is now being planted over wide areas of the United States.

*Red Prince.* Edwin C. Gould selected a limb sport on a Delicious tree from the Horner Orchard of Martinsburg, W. Va. in 1954. The fruit was an early bright red color, a blush type. Edward and Henry Miller of Paw Paw, W. Va., propagated the variety extensively and an Eastern nursery now holds propagation rights.

*Evarts Red.* This strain was discovered in Russel Evart's Starking orchard in Mitamora, Mich. by Roy Gibson of Monroe, Mich. some time before 1950. It is of early red color and has prominent stripes.

*Skyline Supreme.* This variant was discovered by William E. Dalton in his orchard at Hendersonville, N.C. about 1955. It is a whole tree sport in a Starking block. The tree is standard in size but is reported to have a tendency to develop many fruit spurs. The fruit is blush type, solid red, and colors early. It is also reported to *mature* ahead of such strains as Richared and Starking. Plantings have been heavy, especially in the eastern apple growing districts.

*Ryan Red.* In Wapato, Wash., James Ryan observed a limb sport on a Starking tree in his orchard about 1953. The color is mainly blush, but there is evidence of some striping. It is one of the earlier coloring sports and also one of the darkest. There is perhaps a tendency to small fruit size but this might be of no particular disadvantage. It is a good strain and has recently been planted extensively in the Lower Yakima Valley.

*Harrold Red.* A limb sport on a 12 year old Starking was found in 1954 by Wayne Harrold in his orchard near Zillah, Wash. The fruit colored earlier and darker than Starking and was of a stripe type. It is propagated and widely planted in British Columbia and is well accepted. Although not extensively grown in Washington, it has been satisfactory.

*Topred.* This sport is one of the newer standard type trees with stripe type fruit of good color. It was observed first by Leonard Hutchinson as a limb sport on his Shotwell Delicious near Tonasket, Wash. in 1954. Judging by early performance and by new plantings, this variety is currently one of the favorites.

*Imperial Double Red.* L.R. Frazier and Phil Jenkins observed a whole tree sport 14 years old in the Elon Gilbert orchard near Parker, Wash. in 1954. The color, blush type, developed earlier and better than Starking in the same orchard. This sport has been promoted actively and propagations and plantings have been extensive. It is on the way, from present evidence, to becoming a leading variety.

*Houser Red.* This variant started as a bud sport on a mature Starking and was discovered by Lawrence E. Houser in his Selah, Wash. orchard in 1956. It is earlier coloring and darker than Starking, and is of a blush or solid type.

## SPUR TYPE SPORTS

*Okanoma.* A spur-type tree in a Delicious orchard belonging to Mrs. Nettie Knopp of Omak, Wash. was observed to bear better colored fruit. Characteristically the color is blush but some striping may be present. The variety, called "Okanoma", was propagated by a nursery in Oregon and, when the trees were available, the ordering customer refused them. About 200 of these trees were planted near Omak and apparently a planting of similar size near Sawyer, Wash. In the meantime, the Columbia and Okanogan Nursery, Wenatchee, Wash. tested the variety but did not increase it. Not until about 1950 was there any particular interest in this variety, and this coincided with efforts to collect new apple sports at the Irrigation Experiment Station, Prosser, Wash. In checking on the known apple sports, it was found that the planting at Omak had done well.

On learning from the Station nearby about a spur type, early coloring Delicious, Carl Brader of Prosser made a trip to Omak and purchased trees and budwood for his own use. Attention was called to the orchard at Sawyer which compared favorably with Starking. Historically, this was a very significant time considering the eventual interest in spur types, not only in Red Delicious but in Goldens and other varieties as well. It may be stated truly that Okanoma represents the first variety in the current red sport, spur type tree era.

Though commercially planted to some extent, other better coloring types have taken its place, either by topworking or in new plantings. In all fairness, however, if properly spaced, properly grown and harvested, Okanoma is a good Delicious apple. Comparative production costs have been satisfactory. While it will never be a leading variety, it must be duly respected for its spectacular role in apple history—more for what it did than for what it is.

**Starkrimson.** Never satisfied, man is ever searching for something better, and the search for an apple even more nearly perfect than the Starking resulted in the discovery of the Starkrimson, a super Delicious bud sport declared by leading fruit growers to be the "fruit sensation of the century." Like its illustrious Delicious ancestors, the Starking also began to show one fault. The usual high color would be lacking in some years when unfavorable conditions were present. This resulted in a

Starking crop which was not 100% Extra Fancy and Fancy for color.

Growers were alerted to watch for any indication of a super Starking budsport in their orchards, an apple that would have the same aristocratic long shape, the five distinctive points, but with more color under conditions favorable or unfavorable. The search was instigated and backed by Paul Stark, Jr. of Stark Nurseries, who expended every effort to inspect each promising bud sport whenever reported.

Finally in 1951 Roy Bisbee of Hood River, Ore. discovered that every apple on one of his Starking trees was redder than the fruit of the other Starking trees in his orchard, and that it was a month ahead of the usual coloring period. Believing that he had found what Paul Stark was looking for, he budded some limbs of other trees to see if the strain would remain true to type. The experiment showed every apple of the second generation trees to be Extra Fancy in grade and coloring a month earlier, even under unfavorable conditions.

Notified of this bud sport, Stark went to examine the tree. To his great delight the tree showed even better characteristics than first reported. Finding no weak points after inspection of the fruit, bearing habits, and sturdiness, he wired the nursery, "This is it—the Super Sport tree we have been looking for—am starting negotiations for its purchase." And indeed he did. The tree was bought for the highest price ever paid for one tree up to that time—the sum of $25,000.

Not only is the Starkrimson fruit superb, but in addition the tree is of an entirely new and different type. It is abundantly covered with fruit spurs all over the inside and outside, even up and down the main limbs of the tree. Sufficient "resting" spurs are present each year to assure a crop the following season. This *natural* dwarf tree is about two-thirds the size of a standard tree.

Many scientists, marketing experts and leading growers in many apple sections have recognized in the spur-type tree one of the greatest gifts, if not the most outstanding, that Mother Nature has ever given to the apple industry. In Yakima, Wash. Starkrimson trees planted 10 feet apart in rows 20 feet apart produced 400 bushels per acre when the trees were in the fourth year.

In summing up the findings and observations on this apple, there are many good points. Of seven bud sports tested by Marvin Sundquist in the Yakima Valley, Wash., the Starkrimson had the highest ratings for: earliness of coloring, ultimate color formation throughout tree (and at unfavorable locations on tree) typiness, earliness of bearing, volume of fruit produced on test trees up to 1963, and, general uniformity of fruit.

*Redspur.* The fruit color of this sport is a bright red blush. It was first found by L.R. Frazier and Phil Jenkins in the Elon J. Gilbert orchard near Parker, Wash. in 1954. The tree was in a Starking planting. At the present time the variety is one of the favorite spur types and plantings have been extensive.

*Wellspur.* In 1953 Lester Green, of Wells and Wade Fruit Company near Azwell, Wash. discovered three sport trees in a Starking planting that had spur type growth. They bore fruit of good color and of a blush type. Three nurseries in Washington are actively promoting the variety and it has been extensively planted.

*Hardispur.* After the severe early fall freeze of 1955, only one apple tree in the orchard of "Scotty" Griffith of Dryden, Wash. survived. It was a spur type tree of blush type, early coloring Delicious. At one time the variety was called "Lonely". In respect to its survival, it was named Hardispur. Two Washington nurseries propagated it, but at present the variety is not being widely planted.

*Miller Sturdyspur.* This spur type tree was discovered by Gilbert Miller in an orchard of Delicious near Cumberland, Maryland about 1953. It was a whole tree sport about 17 years old. Fruit colors very early and is blush with no stripes. This is one of the newer strains but has been rather widely planted in the East and Midwest.

*Royal Stewart.* The origin of this sport is not known for certain. It has been claimed that W.W. Stewart, of Stewart Brothers Nurseries, Ltd., Kelowna, B.C., observed a limb sport on a 32 year old tree near Kelowna, in 1954. The parent variety was not stated. The Royal Stewart bears early coloring fruit of blush type. It has been extensively propagated in British Columbia and is one of the leading varieties in the Okanogan area, with some plantings elsewhere in the Northwest. Tests and observations have indicated that Royal Stewart is very similar, if not identical to Starkrimson.

*Oregon Spur (Oregon Red) (Red King Spur).* This new discovery in the Wayne Trumbull orchard at Milton-Freewater in Oregon has had a rapid rise in popularity. This may be due to the overstripe color factor and the wide spreading growth characteristic of the tree.

*Earlistripe* and *Regal Red* are limb sports of Wellspur found in the Cal Cooper Orchard, Pateros, Wash. Both are reputed to color their fruit earlier than the parent and are being sold by a Washington nursery.

*Atwood Spur* is a limb sport of Delicious found in the Charles Atwood Orchard, Monitor, Wash. It is a blush type and is being propagated by a Washington nursery.

For a more complete list of Delicious strains see Extension Mimeo 3120 (June 1969) by R.B. Tukey and J. K. Ballard of the Washington State Extension Service, Pullman, also Extension Mimeo 3124 by the same authors published in July, 1969.

FIG. 1.    The Wilder Medal of the American Pomological Society awarded to
Richared in 1953.

# V. GOLDEN DELICIOUS*

## VIRGINIA MAAS

### Tacoma, Washington

IN 1914, WHILE MEN FROM ALASKA TO NEW GUINEA WERE digging in the hills and mountains and panning along the creeks for an elusive yellow mineral, Anderson H. Mullins was unwittingly growing a golden fortune on his 36 acre farm in Clay County, W. Virginia. This tree was destined to bring wealth to growers not only in the United States, but also in Holland, Germany and other countries of Europe, as well as in South Africa, Tasmania and New Zealand.

This bonanza, the spectacular Golden Delicious, was one of the most important developments in the history of the apple industry during the past 50 years, and according to Edwin Gould, Superintendent of University of West Virginia Experimental Fruit Farm, has had "greater impact on this industry than any other single factor."

Actual origin of this nature-bred seedling has been open to conjecture, but thorough research has strongly indicated that it was pollen-sired by an oldtime apple from Virginia called Golden Reinette, the seed being borne in a Grimes Golden apple. The presence of the Golden Reinette trees was explained by Mr. Mullins. His father had bought a few of these trees from an itinerant peddler who came through the Porters Creek area in the 1880's selling trees of several apple varieties, including this one yellow type.

Mullins' father had planted the trees along the pasture fence back of the house. When the fruit matured and dropped to the ground, many seedling trees came up and apparently survived the trampling hooves. Thus, a small insignificant orchard, began

---

The author is indebted to Edwin Gould, Supt. University Experimental Farm, Kearneysville, W. Va. for the section on Spur Types.

but to those recording only items of historical moment, the one important seedling which subsequently sprang up among them and grew to maturity was the original Golden Delicious.

Every time a seed is planted, a new variety will appear, but the chances of it being anything spectacular are many thousands to one. It can happen, however, anytime, anywhere, and if it does the grower has a gold mine in his backyard. The Golden Delicious proved that such an occurrence is not only a possibility, but an actuality.

When Anderson Mullins first noticed this precocious sapling covered with huge apples, he was unaware of its potential. For nine years it bore fruit that was unlike any seen in the entire area, and became locally famous as Mullins Yellow Seedling.

The unique keeping quality of the fruit, its size and sunshine color, combined with its popularity with all who tasted it, finally convinced Mullins that these apples were definitely out of the ordinary. He sent three of them to the Stark Nurseries in Louisiana, Mo., explaining in his letter that not only did this special tree have fruit when others were barren, but that the apples kept in good condition in his dirt-floor cellar until late spring.

It was the month of April, 1914 when Mullins made his decision to mail the three golden apples. Arrival of this package at the nursery sent Paul Stark racing by train, horse, and muleback over the thousand and twenty miles with the earnest desire of a Sir Galahad in a quest for a new apple variety that would be a worthy running mate for the celebrated red Delicious. A perfect yellow apple in April that looked like a Grimes Golden, but with a different flavor, and the conic shape of the red Delicious, was an exciting stranger that might attract the public eye.

When Paul Stark's body-bruising journey terminated at the Mullins place, the mountaineer farmer was not at home. Paul decided to look around on his own. Nothing noteworthy was evident. Recounting the story later, he said, "Back of the house I saw an orchard. But, here came the dismal disappointment! Every tree I could see was nothing but a wild seedling—miserable runts. Dejected and sick at heart, I turned around to leave, when I saw it. There looming forth in the midst of the small, leafless, barren trees, was one with rich green foliage that looked as if it had been transplanted from the Garden of Eden."

The boughs, laden with glorious, golden fruit, were bending to the ground under the weight of the tremendous crop. Almost afraid to examine it more closely for fear it might be only a Grimes Golden tree, he went slowly toward it. Eagerly, but with some misgivings, he reached out for the fruit. When he bit into the tender, crisp, juicy flesh, he knew his quest was over.

He had finished the tangy-flavored morsel, before he saw Mr. Mullins climbing the hillside pasture orchard.

"Give you five thousand dollars for the tree", Stark said without preamble.

"She's yours", Mullins said.

Believing, that this new apple would be more readily accepted by the public if it were associated with the prestige already established for the red Delicious, Stark named the apple Golden Delicious. He wasted no time in cutting budsticks to take home and making arrangements for an iron cage to be built around the tree. This precautionary measure was to prevent any one from stealing propagating material.

This padlocked, sturdy structure on the 30-feet-square piece of land, now owned by Starks, even enclosed the top of tree with woven-steel. A lead-encased wire was strung from the cage down the hillside to the Mullins farmhouse, and a battery-powered burglar alarm was attached to the wire.

To do justice to the honesty of the neighbors, the alarm went off only once. It was a dark night when it alerted the Mullins family to the presence of an intruder. With swinging lanterns, and prepared for battle with a host of thieves, the conscientious guardians of the golden apple rushed up the hillside. The expected host of robbers turned out to be but a single culprit—and a female one at that—quietly chewing, not an apple, but her cud, as she leaned against the wire enclosure. It was the family cow.

Probably no other cage of its type could, years later, claim the distinction of appearing in photograph form on bank checks as did this one in West Virginia in 1958. The picture of the original Golden Delicious tree, bearing fruit and safely ensconsed behind wire, was printed on a centennial issue of between 50,000 and 100,000 checks put out by the Clay County Bank, just prior to the death of the tree.

This was a suitable tribute to an apple about which Professor Ralston of Virginia Agricultural Experiment Station had said, "I am frank to admit that I have never heard leading horticulturists praise any other apple as highly as they have the Golden Delicious."

When the first three apples from Mullins were received at Stark Nurseries, one of them was sent to the late Col. G. B. Brackett, U. S. Pomologist, Washington, D.C. With great excitement he hurried into the office with a little slab of the apple perched on his knife blade, exclaiming to a co-worker, "Taste this! Here's an apple with an even better flavor than Grimes Golden."

The mother tree of the red Delicious boasts of a granite monument erected in honor of its advent, but the original Golden Delicious tree, reduced by death to only a dry stump a few feet high, remains on its remote hillside, unvisited and not easily accessible to curiosity-seekers, or to those who would pay it homage. One group of interested people in 1964, however, did commemorate its discovery. The Department of Horticulture, University of West Virginia, sponsored a 50-year anniversary meeting of horticulturists. Many noted pomologists attended and took part in the program which was held at Morgantown, West Virginia. It was mentioned that this tree during its lifetime had borne a yearly crop of 12 to 15 bushels.

According to some reports, a gavel was once carved from its wood by C.N. Bishop of Frankford, W. Va. This momento can be found in the Capitol Building Museum of the Department of Archives and History. A sign indicating that the Golden Delicious originated in Clay County is located some 15 miles away on the grounds of the Clay County Courthouse.

In the opinion of John T. Bregger, retired horticulturist and nurseryman, "The Golden Delicious is a unique apple in many respects. It not only is the heaviest-planted yellow apple today in America, but is now one of the two or three most popular apples in the world. A carload of them was won as a prize by the world champion St. Louis Cardinal baseball team in 1926. It is commercially grown in most, if not all, apple districts of all five continents. It has wide adaptation to soil and to climate though reaching nearest to perfection in areas of low humidity during the summer. In Southern France, it now comprises over 90% of the new apple plantings. It is also gaining popularity in Italy and Australia."

Though worldwide, Golden Delicious is a typical American variety. In the Tasmanian Journal of Agriculture, Feb. 1963, T.D. Raphail, Senior Horticulturist, and R. Letters, District Horticultural Officer, have said, "Few varieties of apple have increased more rapidly in popular favor and worldwide acceptance in recent years than the Golden Delicious. The production in Tasmania at present is in the vicinity of 86,000 bushels per annum, and could reach 200,000 during the next five or six years.

The first Golden Delicious to be recorded in Tasmania were in the form of grafts in an old orchard at Youngtown in 1930. Soon the popularity of this apple became apparent, though not as great in some districts as in others, doubtless due to climatic conditions. In certain localities difficulty is often experienced in getting adequate early color on the normally red and striped varieties, and the yellow-green type is a valuable alternative.

The excellent eating quality, good flavor and juiciness make it a first-rate dessert fruit, but also a multi-use apple, popular for salads, juice, sauce, pie, or baking, and readily accepted by the babyfood processors.

Vigorous, and with no structural faults, the tree is adaptable for many types of pruning—European espalier method, or standard modified leader system as used in the U.S. With good care, it bears young and regularly, and responds well to thinning, bearing very large fruits under favorable conditions. Because of its long, strong stem and clinging characteristic, it matures heavy crops with minimum losses during windstorms. Another reason it is such an acceptable variety is its adaptability to dwarfing rootstocks.

Breeders are using Golden Delicious as a parent for new apple hybrids. From Japan we have Mutsu (called Crispin in England) a Golden-Indo cross that shows great promise as a multipurpose apple. Some of the U. S. hybrids include such named varieties as Spigold, Jonagold and Sungold. From Summerland B.C. comes Summerred, a promising summer variety, which is out of McIntosh x Golden breeding. In 1969, the Minnesota Station named two hybrids of Golden Delicious, namely Honeygold and Red Baron.

Many selections of Golden Delicious have been made in an attempt to secure a more russet-resistant type. There are also the closely related types, Blushing Golden, Prime Gold and Flaming Gold. In some way perhaps related to the Golden, they will always be associated with the general class of yellow fall and winter apples. The spur-type Golden Delicious will be covered in a separate section.

The adaptability of Golden Delicious to various climates is illustrated by the fact that it bears even in southern Arkansas, a section that is supposed to be out of the winter-apple belt. Trees in Nicollet County, Minn. bore fruit despite a 30 below zero temperature.

Bearing abundant pollen and blooming over a long period, Golden Delicious is a good pollinizer for nearly all commercial varieties. At that Fiftieth anniversary ceremony at Morgantown, Dr. Frank P. Cullinan, Associate Director of USDA Crops Research Division said this apple was one of the best varieties for setting a crop, and is practically self-fruitful.

According to W.A. Luce, retired Yakima County Tree Fruit Agent in Washington State, "The heavy bearing tendency, due to its being self-fruitful, often causes it to become biennial in bearing, but modern chemical thinning methods at blossom and postblossom periods have done much to overcome this fault.

Golden Delicious also has a tendency to russet. Spray burn, as well as cool, damp weather during the early stages of fruit growth, can cause this skin russeting. When spraying, precautionary methods should be used to assure rapid drying, and night spraying should be avoided. High late summer humidity is often responsible for lenticel russeting."

The Golden Delicious apple will sometimes shrivel in storage when not grown under conditions where the skin becomes waxy. A dry, irrigated district stimulates the development of the waxy skin that gives it a most ideal texture and appearance. Northwestern United States and the lower Rhone Valley of France are two such areas. Parts of Italy and Australia also appear to be very desirable for the same reason. Golden Delicious has won wide acclaim in Italy, according to John Bregger who has travelled extensively there. For prolonged storage it is generally necessary to provide conditions that will lessen the tendency to shrivel. Packers have found that early packing and the use of a polyethylene liner in the box does much to eliminate late storage shrivel.

Richard Bantram, Extension Service, Wenatchee, Wash. recommends picking Golden Delicious in the period 135 to 150 days after full bloom. Both earlier and later dates give poorer fruit quality. The best time to pick appears to be as soon as the fruits have lost their green skin color and have turned to light yellow. In contrast to red Delicious, the soluble solids do not increase in stored Golden Delicious. Dips, sprays, or wraps containing Ethoxyquin are recommended for scald control where storage (31 F) is to be for seven months or longer.

Controlled atmosphere (CA) storage has not been as successful with this variety as with McIntosh and Delicious. Grey mold is one of the problems encountered. In the Pacific Northwest cold storage at 31 F and nearly 100% humidity is the most common system. Polyethylene liners are used in the containers. Fruits with a trace of green in skin color at picking time are held for late spring sales, but sometimes bitter pit and storage scald are troublesome.

In 1921 the American Pomological Society awarded their Wilder Medal to the Golden Delicious, the only yellow apple in history to receive this honor. The Wilder Medal was provided by a special trust fund left in 1886 by the late Marshall P. Wilder, scientist and pomologist, who was President of the American Pomological Society for 38 years. He left instructions that it was to be awarded to a fruit only after exhaustive investigation had produced proof of that fruit's supreme merit. This medal was struck off on the presses of the United States mint by special order.

American Fruit Growers Inc. of Allegheny County, Penn., the largest orchard company in the world with a capital of $50,000,000, named their finest orchard in honor of the Golden Delicious. Unlike the red Delicious, whose value was not recognized immediately, the Golden Delicious interested orchardists and national leaders in horticulture in almost every section of the U. S. shortly after its introduction by Stark Nurseries. All were impressed and convinced that this was the most remarkable yellow apple yet known to the fruit world. Quotations from noted growers in practically every state extoll this great apple.

Professor Frederick Cranefield, then Secretary of Wisconsin Horticultural Society, commented that the "horticultural writers and pomologists will have to revise their books on apples because Golden Delicious bears regularly on NEW ONE-YEAR WOOD."

According to Professor W. J. Green of the Ohio Experiment Station, the early and heavy crop-producing characteristics insure the tree coming into profitable bearing on a large scale much earlier than usual. This makes it an ideal apple for orchardists who want quick returns.

During a visit in the U.S. in the 1920's, Queen Marie of Roumania was asked to pose for a photograph. At first she was reluctant, but when she saw the rest of the Royal Party eagerly eating the Golden Delicious apples presented for their consumption, she smilingly selected one of the big, golden beauties, tasted its unusual delicious flavor and then told them to "bring on the camera." The picture is reproduced in *The Stark Story*, the Sept. 1966 Bulletin of the Missouri Historical Society.

Stark Nurseries were so confident that the Golden Delicious would become a universal favorite with the apple-conscious public that they arranged for the planting of a large number of 250-tree demonstration orchards in various sections of the country. In Cashmere, Wash. a grower, whose third-year planting provided a good crop, found that his local packing house would not buy the fruit because "they were unknown and yellow and wouldn't sell." Starks begged the orchardist not to cut down this demonstration orchard and promised to buy his crop for the next three years at a top price. However, it turned out that they had to buy but one crop as the New York buyers took the entire crop at premium prices the succeeding years. Extra Fancy Golden Delicious have topped the market year after year.

It took just such an apple to achieve the notable distinction of proving to fruit buyers and to the fruit retailers, periodical "The Trade", that the public will buy yellow apples—if the apples are good enough. Previous to the introduction of Golden Delicious,"The Trade" declared that they could not sell an apple of that color.

An unsolicited letter to Stark Nurseries from C.A. Lick of Fort Smith, Arkansas, prior to 1929, gives further proof of this public acceptance of yellow apples. In this correspondence Mr. Lick told of his first taste of Golden Delicious on board ship where both this variety and red apples were served in the dining room. He was sufficiently impressed by the flavor to inquire of the head steward where they had been purchased. He was told that 75 boxes of them had been bought in New York at a cost of $5.75 per box. Mr. Lick ended the letter by saying that the boxes lasted the 325 passengers less than half the cruise and that nobody ate red apples while the yellow ones were still available.

If Mullins' cow had eaten the seedling tree, or if Mullins had not sent the sample fruit to Stark Nurseries, or if Paul Stark had not taken the trip to West Virginia, this variety would never have come into existence. One wonders how many other tiny seedlings have struggled against countless odds only to find their unfoldment unnoticed and undiscovered.

## SPUR-TYPE SPORTS

A total of 34 selections of spur type Golden Delicious have been discovered and are now (1967) under evaluation. Available information indicates that 24 already have been planted in commercial orchards. These selections were discovered mostly in groups of two or more per orchard. Fourteen selections were discovered in one orchard. Selections have been found in a total of 11 orchards. Accurate detailed records as to the origin and development of these various selections leaves much to be desired. The information which is available, however, is of interest and serves as a basis for the theories of origin.

*Gilbert.* There are two selections involved in this orchard. They were the first of the semidwarf spur type mutations of Golden Delicious to be discovered. They were found by Phil Jenkins, the production manager, in an orchard owned by Elon Gilbert and located near Parker, Wash. In many respects these two selections are the most interesting of the spur types. They occurred as adjacent trees in a block which was set in the spring of 1955. The original trees were McIntosh on standard seedling rootstock. They were topworked to Golden Delicious in the spring of 1956. This was intended to give a McIntosh framework for winter hardiness. The length of the McIntosh section varied as much as 12 inches or more. Available information was that multiple grafts were made on both trees and that all of them developed the typical spur-type growth characteristics. This would support the general belief that the mutation must have been in the scion wood. This, however, raises the question as to how all the scaffolds on both trees could have been worked with scions from the same limb or tree without its being distributed to any of the other trees in the block. It also raises the question as to the source of the mutation scion wood and when the mutation occurred.

All scaffolds of both trees appeared to be identical. In the orchard, however, only one tree was used as a source of scion wood. But the scionwood was taken from all branches of the selected tree. This selection was patented and is now in commercial development under the trade name Starkspur.

*Sundale.* The second series of natural genetic semidwarf spur type mutations of Golden Delicious was discovered by Grady Auvil in 1960. There were four trees involved in this instance. They appeared as whole trees in the Sundale Orchard near Roosevelt, Wash. It was set in 1954. These trees were located in a block of Golden Delicious on standard seedling rootstocks. The trees in this block froze back to ground level during the fall of 1955. In the spring of 1956 they were cut off and grafted. It could not readily be determined for all trees whether the scions were set in the rootstock or in a section of the original Golden Delicious. Available evidence, however, indicates that they were all redeveloped with a section of the original Golden Delicious between the seedling and the mutation. The time and place of this mutation is not known. It seems logical to conclude that all four trees developed from a single mutation which had occurred before the grafting was done. If this is true then all four selections should be genetically identical. It is entirely possible, however, that the mutations may have occurred after the grafting was done making all of the selections genetically different. A major factor discounting this latter theory is that all of the recognized spur-type mutations of Golden Delicious were found in the State of Washington following the destructive fall freeze of 1955. The wide distribution of the various selections does not support the theory of a common origin. The fact that most of the selections occurred in groups would indicate that the selections within such groups may well have had a common origin. Regardless of time or place of origin all four trees appear identical from the standpoint of tree characteristics as well as fruiting habits. Thus they were considered as a single clone in patent application as well as in commercial development. They are in commercial development under the trade names, Goldspur and Hardyspur.

*Thornton.* There were 14 spur-type trees recognized in this case. All occurred as whole trees in a block of Golden Delicious owned by Oscar Thornton, Orville, Wash. The block was set in 1956. The stock for this planting was propagated by the Heath Nursery, Pateros, Wash. The mutations were first recognized in 1961. The 14 trees were widely scattered throughout the planting. There was a wide variation in the size and vigor of the various selections. In growth characteristics however, all appeared to be comparable. It is possible, but hardly probable, that part or all of these selections may have been replants. Since all of these selections occurred as whole trees, the time and place of the mutation is unknown. They may all have had a common origin or they may represent separate distinct mutations. It would seem logical to conclude, however, that all had a common origin and that the mutation had occurred before the nursery stock was budded and thus introduced through the budstick. So far as known only one other spur-type tree (Thompson) developed from a substantial quantity of Golden Delicious stock from the same nursery distributed in 1956. Available information indicates that all of the selections are identical but they have not yet (1967) been thoroughly evaluated. Since they do appear to be identical they are in commercial development as a single selection under the trade name Yellospur.

*Thompson.* This selection arose as a whole tree in the Ronald Thompson orchard, Orville, Wash. It is located in a block of Golden Delicious which was set in 1956. It is possible, but hardly probable, that this select tree was a replant. It was first recognized in 1961. Information pertaining to its origin and development is the same as that for the Thornton selections. It should be recognized however, that this selection may have originated as a separate mutation and thus be genetically different from the Thornton selections, but it was considered as having had a common origin with the Thornton selections and was introduced commercially under the same trade name.

*Frazer.* This selection occurred as a tree in a block of Golden Delicious in an orchard owned by Loren Frazer, Parker, Wash. The planting was made in 1954. The mutation was first recognized in 1961. It is possible that this tree was a replant but there is not valid information to support this conclusion. If this tree was in the original planting it would be of special significance indicating that the mutation either occurred before the 1955 freeze or else it is a specific mutation which originated in the orchard location.

*Morrison.* This selection also occurred as a whole tree in a block of Golden Delicious owned by Charles Morrison, Zillah, Wash. This block was also set in 1954. The mutation was first recognized in 1962. This selection represents a situation similar to that recorded for the Frazer selection. It is possible that this selection was a replant, but, if not, it would indicate that the mutation occurred either before the 1955 freeze or else it is a distinct mutation which occurred in the orchard after the tree was set.

*Elliot.* There are two selections involved in this case. They occurred as whole trees in an orchard owned by M. W. Elliot, Parker, Wash. They were propagated on EM VII rootstock and are interplants of 1959 in a block of standard Golden Delicious set in 1956. The two spur type mutations occurred on the interplanted stock. They were first recognized in 1963. These selections are of special interest from the standpoint of time and place of origin. If the theory that the 1955 freeze was a factor in producing the spur type mutations of Golden Delicious then the results would indicate that the mutation reflected in these selections occurred before they were budded in the nursery. If they originated as specific separate mutations, they would discredit the theory of a specific factor and time (1955 freeze) in the mutation of the various recognized strains. It would also indicate a variation in the factors responsible for this distinct type of mutation. The nursery stock for this planting came from the Morrison Nursery. It might be significant that a similar spur type mutation developed in the Morrison orchard prior to the propagation of the stock for this planting. This could indicate a possible source of spur type budwood in the nursery operation. It is conceivable that all three selections had a common undetermined origin. These two trees represent the oldest recognized spur type Golden Delicious mutations on dwarfing rootstocks.

*Templin.* There are three selections involved. They occurred in orchards belonging to Graydon Templin, Manson, Wash. They were first observed in 1963. One of these selections developed as a single graft on an old Jonathan tree. The other two selections occurred as whole trees in a block of Golden Delicious. Available information indicates that this block of trees was set about 1951. It is possible, however, that these selections may have been replants. Since the exact age of these trees could not be determined, they afford little support for any theory as to time and place of origin of the mutation.

*Columbia River Orchard Company.* There are three selections recognized in this case. All developed as trees in widely scattered blocks of Golden Delicious in the orchard operations of the Columbia River Orchard Company, Wenatchee, Wash.

*Schell.* There are two and probably three selections recognized in this case. They are of special interest from the standpoint of time and place of origin. If they prove to be true spur type mutations they will be the first for which the approximate time and place of origin is known. These selections originated in a block of Golden Delicious which was set in 1920. The mutations originated in a similar manner at points near heavy branch cuts high on upright scaffolds. They appear to have originated from adventitious buds near the point of the cut. There were two limbs involved in one tree. They originated at approximately the same time and in a similar manner near the point where the cut had been made. The two branches originated some five inches apart. Only one of these branches however, was selected for evaluation studies. The third branch on the second tree originated in a similar manner. All three branches were comparable in size and general appearance. They were three to five inches in diameter and five to six feet in length. They appeared to be about eight years old when first recognized in 1964. They originated in the Clarence Schell orchard near Cashmere, Wash. It is one of the oldest blocks of Golden Delicious still in production. Because of age and low vigor of the trees, it was difficult to accurately evaluate the select limbs. The characteristics of these selections are not as distinctive as those of the other selections which arose as individual trees. Second generation trees however, support the indications that they are true mutations but more study will be required for complete evaluation.

The first spur type bud sport of Golden Delicious was discovered in 1959. The Worthen* sport, originating about 1953, did not turn out to be a true spur-type. Since then a total of 34 have been recognized and brought under evaluation. It seems logical to expect the discovery of additional selections. Undoubtedly many selections have been destroyed without having been recognized. All but two of the recognized selections occurred as whole trees. Thus, the time and place of origin is unknown. It is significant to note that all of the recognized selections appeared at approximately the same time following the destructive late fall freeze in 1955. It is highly important to note that there is no significant difference between any of the recognized selections. Of special concern is the development of a distinctive type of reversion or mixture in certain selections indicating the possibility of genetic instability. Regardless of the origin or stability of the new spur type Golden Delicious, it promises to be a factor of major importance in the future of the fruit industry in all areas where the variety is grown.

*Frank Worthen Orchard, Maches Hgts., near Yakima, Wa.

FIG. 1.   Standard Golden Delicious.
          (Courtesy, Washington State Fruit Commission)

FIG. 2.   Spur-type Golden Delicious (Starkspur)
(Courtesy, Stark Nurseries)

# VI. JONATHAN

R.P. LARSEN
Tree Fruit Research Center,

Washington State University,
Wenatchee, Washington

IN 1845, A.J. DOWNING WROTE "THE JONATHAN IS A VERY beautiful dessert apple, and its great beauty, good flavour, vigorous growth and productiveness unite to recommend it to orchard planters. The original tree of this new sort is growing on the farm of Mr. Philip Rick, of Kingston, N.Y., a neighbourhood unsurpassed in the world for its great congeniality to the apple" (6, p. 113–4).

The first published account of Jonathan was in 1826 when it was described by Judge J. Buel of Albany, N.Y. and listed as the New Esopus Spitzenberg or Ulster Seedling. In 1829 Judge Buel sent specimens of the fruit to the Massachusetts Horticultural Society indicating it was an Esopus seedling sometimes called New Spitzenberg (1, p. 172–5). It was named Jonathan by Judge Buel in honor of Jonathan Hasbrouck who first called his attention to the variety (1, p. 172–5, p. 113–4).

The value of the Jonathan was recognized also in other apple areas of the east, midwest and west and it soon became accepted as a desirable variety. During the first year of the Michigan Pomological Society in 1870, Jonathan was extolled as, "a very choice apple, a good keeper and of excellent quality—the chief value of this apple is that it is an annual and abundant bearer; there are always apples where there are Jonathan apple trees"(8, p. 11–14).

By 1874, Jonathan was listed first as a winter market apple recommended by the Michigan Pomological Society (9, p. 15). The 1900 Report of the Michigan State Horticultural Society (10, p. 108), which superseded the Michigan Pomological Society, continued to recommend Jonathan as, "one of the best for market. Bright red, good quality, commands a good price."

In 1905, Beach (1, p. 172–5) described Jonathan as being a beautiful brilliant red color, with high flavored and excellent quality fruit of the Esopus Spitzenberg class. Beach further stated, "In New York State it does fairly well in favorable localities if grown on rich soil and given careful attention, but even under such circumstances it does not usually attain as good size as it does in certain portions of the valleys of the Ohio, Mississippi and Missouri and in the irrigated districts in the mountain regions farther west."

Thus, the Jonathan seemed to have a natural "congeniality" to the midwest, west, and certain areas of Pennsylvania and the Virginias. By the turn of the century, it was well established as the leading variety in Michigan and one of the leading varieties in several other states. The major "Jonathan" states for 50 or more years, have been Michigan, Washington, Illinois, Colorado, Ohio and Pennsylvania.

During the first part of this century, Jonathan was the sixth most important variety, next to Baldwin, Ben Davis, Northern Spy, Rhode Island Greening and Winesap (12, p. 489). At that time Delicious was not listed as a commercial variety. But by 1928, Delicious had taken over the number one position in tree numbers, with more than one half of its 6.7 million trees being under nine years of age (7, p. 10–13, 13, p. 101–4). At that time the 25 major varieties in 41 states had a total of 65 million trees. Of these, Jonathan accounted for slightly under 6½ million trees or about 10% of the total.

In 1928, Chandler (2, p. 103) wrote, "Jonathan apples are excellent for many culinary purposes. However, the fruit does not usually keep well in storage; and the variety is declining in

importance as a market apple, especially in the box apple section".

The poor storage characteristics of Jonathan can be attributed
to its susceptibility to several functional or physiological disor-
ders, especially internal breakdown and Jonathan spot. Furthermore, these diseases are aggravated by the tendency to harvest
the fruit at an advanced stage of maturity, when it has reached
a maximum of size and red coloration plus good flavor and
mellow texture. Jonathan spot was probably the most prominent and serious disorder affecting keeping and shipping quality
of the fruits until the advent of controlled atmosphere (CA)
storage. Jonathan spot is a skin disorder giving the apple a
speckled appearance from small brown or black spots. The disorder is an indication of overripeness.

Thus, because of Jonathan spot and other undesirable features of the fruit and tree (such as susceptibility to fire-blight),
Jonathan declined in relative importance from about 10% of the
United States apple production in the late 1920's down to about
7% by the 1940's, where it has continued to remain (Table 1).
During the late 1940's and early 50's Jonathan ranked 4th after
Delicious, McIntosh and Winesap. During recent years, however, Golden Delicious and Rome Beauty have passed Jonathan
in total production, but Winesap has declined rapidly and is
now below Jonathan in production.

Also, as Chandler indicated, Jonathan production gradually
declined in the "box apple" areas of the Northwest. Washington
had maintained a close second to Michigan in Jonathan production until the early 1950's. Washington's 10-year average Jonathan production, 1945 to 1954, was 1,472,000 bushels or about
20% of the total national crop (Table 2), but, during the 1962–66
period, Washington's Jonathan production had dropped to
484,000 bushels, or less than 5% of the national Jonathan crop.
During the same periods, Michigan's Jonathan production increased from an average of 1,484,000 bushels in 1945–54 to
3,878,000 bushels during 1962–66, which was 44% of the national crop of this variety (Table 2). Pennsylvania and Ohio

likewise had increases in production, and Jonathan remained a dominant variety in a number of other Midwestern States where the fruit was traditionally sold shortly after harvest or was held a relatively short time in storage.

***Characteristics of Jonathan.*** The trees are medium in size, moderately vigorous, but somewhat slow in achieving sufficient size for heavy production per acre, particularly on lighter soils. The mature trees are roundish, spreading, somewhat drooping and often dense. The bark is reddish brown, or olive green. Leaves are small, grayish green in color, narrow oval in shape, usually folding inward or waved, coarsely pubescent, with coarse, irregular serrations (Fig. 1). Shoots are medium long, slender, usually straight or with slight curvature.

Fig. 1.   Typical leaves and fruit of Jonathan.

Young trees tend to be dense having many small, slender branches. The trees come into fruiting early causing a bending and drooping of the slender growth. The early bearing tendency and the natural dominance of the lower branches often results in a low tree with the central leader being "fruited-out" at an early age. Thus, the trees, particularly those on dwarfing rootstocks, require careful training and other good cultural practices to insure that they reach sufficient height and size for profitable bearing.

Jonathan trees are very susceptible to fireblight, powdery mildew, and cedar rust, but only moderately susceptible to apple scab. They are average in winter hardiness.

The trees bear heavily and annually and are at least partially self-fruitful, even in areas where pollination is a problem. This is the only commercial variety, for example, that can be safely planted in solid blocks in Michigan. Because of their heavy bearing tendency, the trees must be well pruned, receive sufficient nitrogen to insure good vigor and usually should be thinned in order to avoid undersized fruits. Jonathan trees respond well to various cultural manipulations including chemical thinning, fertilizer variations and preharvest drop sprays. But, the fruits of Jonathan are sensitive to climatic and cultural "stresses". For example, poor finish and russeting of the fruit may be associated with a number of factors including: 1) low temperatures (31 F or lower) during the early growth stages from the bloom period for 2 to 3 weeks thereafter, 2) use of certain spray chemicals or chemical combinations during the early growth period, and 3) low nutritional vigor of the trees.

The fruits are usually medium to small in size. The form is roundish conic to ovate, uniform in shape and size (Fig. 1). Stems are slender and medium to long. The stem cavity is acute, deep and wide, usually symmetrical and sometimes slightly furrowed. The calyx is small and closed, and the calyx basin is deep, abrupt and moderately narrow to wide.

The skin is smooth, thin and usually "tough". When well-colored, the fruit is almost completely deep red, or lively, bright red with a pale yellow area around the cavity. Less well-colored fruits are pale to bright yellow overlaid with bright red (Fig. 1). Lenticels are small, usually inconspicuous. Newer red colored bud sports of Jonathan have a consistent, bright red to deep red color and are usually brilliant and very attractive. It is an excellent eating apple with crisp flesh and "sprightly" flavor and is increasingly accepted as a dual purpose fruit for fresh use and processing.

*Future of the Variety.* The long run future of Jonathan was in jeopardy, even in Michigan and other important Jonathan producing states, primarily because of its storage and marketing problems. From approximately 1945 to 1955, the percentage of Jonathan trees planted in Michigan, relative to other varieties, declined steadily. By the early 1950's, Delicious passed Jonathan in numbers of new trees being planted in Michigan; whereas during the 1940's 35% of all apple trees planted in Michigan had been Jonathan and only 22% Delicious (11).

The advent of controlled atmosphere storage has greatly brightened the future outlook for the Jonathan variety because the problems of Jonathan spot, soft scald, and short storage life have been largely overcome. In fact, Jonathans can now be stored at 32 F with a carbon dioxide content of 2.5 to 5.0% with virtually no loss from either Jonathan spot or soft scald (3, p. 452–9, 5, p. 44–9).

Jonathan spot may be avoided by picking before the fruit is overmature and storing it promptly in regular refrigerated storage at 30 to 32 F (4). However, soft scald is a storage disorder that periodically results in considerable economic loss of Jonathans in refrigerated storage held at 30 to 32 F.

Jonathan is particularly susceptible to soft scald, which should not be confused with the common apple scald or storage scald. In its early stages, soft scald may slightly resemble apple scald by faint patches of brown skin, but these develop rapidly into sunken areas of discolored skin with sharp margins between scalded and nonaffected areas. The tissue beneath the affected areas becomes spongy in texture and brown in color. The disorder is sometimes referred to as ribbon scald because of its characteristic ribbon pattern around the fruit. Soft scald is considered by some researchers to be a surface manifestation of soggy breakdown which has been a serious storage problem with Jonathan in Missouri and Iowa.

The great paradox of storing Jonathan under regular refrigeration is that the fruits should be stored at 35 F to prevent the possibility of soft scald, but this temperature will shorten the life and increase the amount of Jonathan spot as compared to lower storage temperatures. In CA, Jonathans are held at 31-32 F in excellent condition for 6 months or more. CA storage controls Jonathan spot and permits low temperature storage without the danger of soft scald. By using low temperatures in controlled atmospheres, by harvesting properly, and by avoiding oversize fruit, the Jonathan variety is now marketed throughout the winter and into the early spring. By 1964 about ½ of Michigan's storage Jonathans were being held in controlled atmospheres (4, p. 97-103).

Thus, Jonathan's image and future has changed in Michigan and other Jonathan producing states. It should also be noted that Jonathan has enjoyed increasing acceptance by processors. Modern cultural practices are sufficiently adaptable so that growers can provide processors with fruits that they want, for example, small fruits for speciality purposes or larger ones for slices. In Michigan, growers have renewed confidence in the Jonathan and have increased the rate of planting in recent years. In the future, Jonathan production will likely increase but, as a variety, it will continue to decline in relative importance to Delicious and Golden Delicious.

## SPORTS*

A number of bud sports of Jonathan have been found which produce fruit of brilliant solid red color and which are usually more acceptable to the consumer than the normal fruits of the original clone. However, the fruits of some sports become excessively dark on trees grown on light soils. Thus growers should carefully evaluate the various Jonathan sports and choose those which are most acceptable for their markets and under their growing conditions. Some of the more important sports are as follows:

*Anderson.* Bud sport of Jonathan, discovered in the Robert Anderson orchard, Covert, Mich. in 1923; selected by Robert Anderson, and Roy Gibson, Greening Nursery Co., Monroe, Mich. and introduced by Greening Nursery Co. in 1927. Fruits are bright red over a yellow ground color.

*Blackjon.* Discovered in the Thomas Slack orchard near Wenatchee, Wash. in 1927 as a limb sport on a regular Jonathan tree. Fruits have deep red color that develops much earlier than Jonathan. It was originated and propagated by Columbia and Okanogan Nursery, Wenatchee, Wash. and trademarked as Blackjon when introduced in 1931 by C and O Nursery.

*Jon-A-Red.* Bud mutation of Jonathan discovered in 1930 in William Uecher orchard, Peshastin, Wash. Fruits have early, overall bright red color. Introduced commercially in 1934 under U. S. Plant Patent #85 by Stark Nurseries, Louisiana, Mo.

*Kingjon.* (King Jonathan). Limb sport on a 50-year-old Jonathan tree, discovered in A.W. King orchard, Wenatchee, Wash. in 1933. The skin colors earlier and darker than Jonathan, at

*Information on sports and hybrids of Jonathan was obtained from: 1) Brooks, R.M. and H.P. Olmo. Register of New Fruit and Nut Varieties. Proceedings of American Society for Horticultural Science, Volumes 45, 56, 72, 78, 81, 83, 85, 87, 89, 91 and 93; 2) Fruit variety bulletins of various state experiment stations and extension services; and 3) Direct communication with nurseries.

first red striped, then becoming solid red. Introduced and propagated by various commercial firms (see Valnur below).

*Valnur* (King Jonathan). Limb sport described above as Kingjon; trademarked, propagated, and sold as Valnur Double Red Jonathan by Van Well Nursery, Wenatchee, Wash.

*All Red.* A bud mutation discovered in 1934 in Allentown, Penn.; selected by Homer S. Kemp and introduced by Bountiful Ridge Nurseries, Princess Anne, Md. in 1937. Fruit color attractive, full bright red but not too dark under eastern conditions.

*Watson.* Bud mutation discovered in 1940 in Vernon, B.C. by J.K. Watson. Fruit with solid blush, bright, attractive. Introduced in 1950.

*Nured.* Early coloring bud sport of Blackjon discovered in 1953 in Columbia and Okanogan Nursery Company's orchard in Wenatchee, Wash. Trees and fruit are like the parent except that fruit reaches full color ten days to two weeks earlier than Blackjon. Introduced commercially in 1965 (at first listed in C and O catalogue as Allred); U.S. Plant Patent applied for.

*Jonnee.* Early coloring bud sport of Blackjon, discovered in 1964 in Caldwell, Idaho by Stanley Robinson and Warren Carnefix. Introduced in 1967 by Hilltop Orchards and Nurseries, Hartford, Michigan (Plant Patent applied for). Trees and fruit are like parent, except fruits larger and color 7–10 days earlier with more intense color than Blackjon.

## HYBRIDS

A great many hybrids of Jonathan have been developed through breeding programs or selected from natural seedlings of Jonathan. None has become established as a major variety in the national apple market, but several have developed into important or promising varieties in certain states or regions. Some of the more popular and promising are as follows:

*Idared.* A cross of Wagener and Jonathan made at the Idaho Agricultural Experiment Station, Moscow; selected in 1935; and introduced commercially in 1942. Fruits are firm, crisp and juicy, of Jonathan flavor, medium-bright red, medium-large in size (2 ½ to 3 ½ inches in diameter), uniform in shape with smooth, light waxy finish, and the flesh is white with an occasional trace of pink. It has good dessert quality, and keeps exceptionally well in common or cold storage, but the fruits may eventually develop Jonathan spot in some seasons.

Trees are moderate in growth and size; the branches grow more upright than Jonathan and are thicker and more sturdy. They are equally as susceptible to fireblight. Idared trees come into bearing early, produce heavily and annually.

This is perhaps the most widely tested and planted Jonathan hybrid. Its popularity as a possible long-storage apple was bright until the great increase in CA storage of the older varieties.

*Webster.* A cross of (Ben Davis x Jonathan) x (Ben Davis x Jonathan) at the New York State Agricultural Experiment Station, Geneva, introduced in 1938. Fruits are large, attractive, red-streaked. Webster has shown particular promise as a fall processing variety. It is a triploid and produces poor pollen so provision must be made to insure ample pollination of adjacent varieties.

*Melrose.* A cross of Jonathan x Delicious at Ohio Agricultural Experiment Station, Wooster, introduced in 1944. Fruits are large, somewhat resemble Jonathan except they are not as well colored and more oblate in shape. They keep well in storage and are satisfactory for both dessert and processing.

*Monroe.* A cross of Jonathan x Rome Beauty at New York Agricultural Experiment Station, Geneva, introduced in 1949. Fruits are larger than Jonathan but similar in color. It has shown particular value as a processing variety for sauce, canning and frozen slices. Trees are quite similar to Jonathan including being susceptible to mildew. They bear early and annually.

Table 1.   Average yearly production of major apple varieties in the
           United States (in million bushels)*

|                   | 1945-54 | 1958-62 | 1962-66 | 1967-68 |
|-------------------|---------|---------|---------|---------|
| Jonathan          | 7.3     | 8.2     | 8.8     | 7.5     |
| Delicious         | 22.3    | 26.5    | 34.1    | 30.8    |
| Winesap           | 11.3    | 8.7     | 7.6     | 5.6     |
| McIntosh          | 10.2    | 17.3    | 15.4    | 14.7    |
| Rome Beauty       | 6.9     | 8.7     | 9.7     | 9.5     |
| Golden Delicious  | 3.2     | 7.5     | 11.2    | 13.6    |
| All varieties     | 105.9   | 123.0   | 128.9   | 117.6   |

*Source:   Statistical bulletins No. 192, September 1956, and Reports of Commercial
           Apple Production by Varieties, 1956, 1959, 1965 and 1968 by U. S. Depart-
           ment of Agriculture, Crop Reporting Board, Washington, D.C. Note that
           1962 is included in both columns 3 and 4.

TABLE 2.   Average yearly production of Jonathan in the United
           States, by major producing states (in bushels x 1000)*

|               | 1945-54 | 1958-62 | 1962-66 | 1967-68 |
|---------------|---------|---------|---------|---------|
| Michigan      | 1,484   | 3,254   | 3,878   | 3,203   |
| Washington    | 1,472   | 565     | 484     | 165     |
| Illinois      | 682     | 582     | 641     | 670     |
| Pennsylvania  | 446     | 604     | 571     | 327     |
| Colorado      | 439     | 375     | 426     | 283     |
| Ohio          | 330     | 559     | 434     | 451     |
| All states    | 7,275   | 8,170   | 8,841   | 7,473   |

*Source: same as Table 1.

*Jonadel.* A cross of Jonathan x Delicious at the Iowa Agricultural Experiment Station, Ames, introduced in 1958. Fruits are larger than Jonathan, equal in red color to Jonathan; ripens with Jonathan; excellent dessert quality; flesh is juicy and firm. Jonadel keeps well in storage with little problem of Jonathan spot or internal breakdown. The trees are similar to Jonathan but more resistant to fireblight.

*Jonalicious.* A chance seedling that resembles Jonathan, discovered in 1933 in Abilene, Texas by Anna Morris Daniels; introduced in 1960 by Stark Nurseries, Louisiana, Mo., Plant Patent No. 1777. Fruit has smooth, thick, tough skin with a yellow ground color overlaid with bright solid red; flesh is juicy, tender crisp, subacid, firm texture, good quality; stores well and late.

*Holiday.* A cross of Macoun x Jonathan at Ohio Agricultural Experiment Station, Wooster, in 1940; introduced in 1964. Fruit resembles Macoun, deep red skin; flesh white, crisp; high dessert quality; keeps well in storage.

*Jonagold.* A cross of Golden Delicious x Jonathan at the Geneva (N.Y.) Agricultural Experiment Station; selected in 1953 and named in 1968. It is a dual purpose apple resembling both parents, scarlet stripe over a yellow ground color. Quality is good and it keeps well in cold storage until spring. It is a triploid, therefore a poor pollinizer for other varieties.

*Spijon.* A cross of Red Spy x Monroe (Jonathan x Rome) at the Geneva (N.Y.) Agricultural Experiment Station, named in 1968. An annual cropper, it is a dual purpose apple which is outstanding as a processor. The fruits are large, of good quality, and have a very attractive red blush. The variety is diploid. It is picked with Rome or later.

## Literature Cited

1. Beach, S.A. 1905. The Apples of New York. Report of the New York Agricultural Experiment Station for the Year, 1903, Vol 1. 409 p.

2. Chandler, W.H. 1928. North American Orchards. Lea and Febiger, Philadelphia. 516 p.

3. Dewey, D.H. 1962. Factors affecting the quality of Jonathan apples stored in controlled atmospheres. Proc. 16th Int. Hort. Congress, Vol 3.

4. Dewey, D.H. 1964. New developments in fruit storage. Mich. State Horticultural Society. 94th annual report.

5. Dilley, D.R. 1964. Maturity and present conditions of apples now in storage. Michigan State Horticultural Society. 94th annual report.

6. Downing, A.J. 1845. The Fruits and Fruit Trees of America. Wiley and Putnam, New York. 594 p.

7. Gourley, J.H. and F.S. Howlett, 1947. Modern Fruit Production. The Macmillan Company, New York. 579 p.

8. Michigan State Pomological Society First Report 1870–71. Remarks on the cultivation and varieties of apples.

9. Michigan State Pomological Society 4th annual report 1874. Winter apples recommended by the society.

10. Michigan State Horticultural Society 30th annual report 1900. Old and new varieties of apples.

11. Michigan Fruit Tree Survey, 1963–65. Michigan Crop Reporting Service of the Michigan and U.S. Departments of Agriculture. Lansing.

12. United States Department of Agriculture Yearbook 1915. Production of apple varieties 1909–1916. U.S. Government Printing Office, Washington, D.C.

13. Youngman, W.H. 1931. Apple-tree plantings since 1920. U.S. Department of Agriculture Yearbook 1931: U.S. Government Printing Office, Washington, D.C.

# VII. McINTOSH*

## W.H. UPSHALL
Director *(retired),*

Horticultural Experiment Station,
Vineland Station, Ontario

THE HISTORY OF THE MCINTOSH APPLE IS INTIMATELY TIED TO that of the McIntosh family. John McIntosh discovered the seedling tree about 1811, recognized its merit, and began to grow for sale seedlings from it about 1820. About 1835 the technique of grafting was learned and from that time on, McIntosh trees bearing fruit identical to the original tree were available from the now well established McIntosh nursery. It was situated near the site of origin of the variety at what is now Dundela, Matilda Township, Dundas County, Ontario, Canada.

John's sons, Allan (1815–1899) and Sandy (1825–1906) carried on the nursery business, in particular the promotion of the McIntosh variety. Allan's son, Harvey, continued in the nursery business. To Allan McIntosh must be given the credit for keeping in his journal a record of the family and of the advancement of the McIntosh apple.

The first printed reference to McIntosh appeared in *Fruits and Fruit Trees of America* by Downing in 1876. It was not until about 1900 that McIntosh became widely known. Probably its marked susceptibility to the scab disease was responsible in part for its slow progress in these early years. The first official Ontario spray calendar for apples was issued in 1895, perhaps

*Adapted in part from the manuscript, *The McIntosh Red: A History and a Development* by Helen Parlow Matheson

about the same time as for other areas on this continent.

The writer recalls eating McIntosh apples from his grandfather's orchard in Port Elgin, Bruce County, Ontario, near Lake Huron, in the first decade of the 20th century. But they were known locally as "Gem", not McIntosh—a more appealing name given perhaps by an enterprising nursery. These trees were planted before the turn of the century.

## THE McINTOSH FAMILY

Alexander McIntosh and family emigrated about 1776 from the Highlands of Scotland to Vischer's Ferry in the Mohawk Valley of New York State. Their youngest son, John, was born there in 1777. When he was 19 years of age (1796) he had a disagreement with his parents over a love affair and left home for Canada. John married Hannah Doran in 1801. For 10 years they farmed along the St. Lawrence River. Then Edward Doran, John's brother-in-law, exchanged farms with him. John's new farm was on the 5th Concession of Matilda Township and several miles from the river.

On this farm about one-fourth acre had been cleared several years previous to 1811 but second growth had come up again to a height of 10 to 12 feet. Among this growth were several apple trees, age unknown, but probably small, for they were saved and later moved to a garden area. By 1830 only one tree remained—the original McIntosh. It goes to prove the hardiness of this variety even from the very beginning.

John McIntosh started to grow seedlings from this hardy choice fruited variety about 1820 and sold the trees to other settlers. Like all fruit seedlings each one was different, some bearing good fruit, others not so good. However, about 1835, an unnamed wanderer came through the area. He knew how to propagate apple trees true to type by budding and grafting and showed the McIntosh family the technique. Soon thereafter only nursery trees truly McIntosh were sold.

As John's farming operations expanded, his wife, Hannah,

took on more responsibility for the orchard and nursery of the McIntosh apple. This resulted in its being called first "Granny's Apple". It was only at a later date (1836) that it became known as McIntosh Red, eventually McIntosh.

About this time, son Allan began to take hold of the nursery business. At first he used McIntosh seedlings as a grafting stock, later the hardier Transcendent Crab. When these seedlings were two or three years old they were taken up in the fall, stored in a cool cellar (no furnaces in those days), and during the winter they were grafted to McIntosh scions from the orchard. The new grafts were stored in moist sawdust in the cellar until planting time in the spring. Sometimes bud grafting (budding) was done on the same kinds of rootstocks in the nursery in July or August. Also, some scions of McIntosh were sold to orchardists who wished to topwork trees in their own orchards.

Allan delivered trees by horse-drawn wagon in both Eastern Ontario and neighboring New York and Vermont States. The Ontario McIntosh family did not lose connection with their relatives in the United States for it is recorded that William McIntosh of West Berlin, Vt. secured a barrel of McIntosh apples from Canada and used these samples to sell McIntosh trees in Vermont. It is known also that Allan himself in 1879, at 64 years of age, took a combined holiday-business trip to the Mohawk Valley. William McIntosh of Vermont planted some McIntosh trees in his own orchard in 1870 which were still bearing fruit in 1930, 60 years later. In 1872 a New York firm was advertising nursery trees of the McIntosh variety. Whether the trees were grown in U.S.A. or in Canada is not known.

Allan McIntosh was quite aware that pollenizers were necessary to get good crops of McIntosh. Therefore, he grew nursery trees of other varieties and sold them for planting with McIntosh. He was also well informed on developments in the control of apple scab and was among the first in Ontario to use fungicides for this purpose. With a homemade wire device, he also dug out borers from the trunks of his trees. Another interesting

McIntosh practice was the draining of orchards through hewn cedar troughs.

Like all of us, Allan had his disappointments. One summer night in 1866 his herd of cattle broke into his nursery, ate off and trampled down nearly all of his foot high apple trees, about 10,000 in number, with a calculated loss of $800—a heavy blow in those days.

The most colorful of the McIntosh clan was Sandy, Allan's youngest brother and 10 years his junior. He was known as "Sandy the Grafter". He would set out each spring with a load of young trees and scions on his back selling his goods and services for cash or for other goods. One time he was known to bring home a cow obtained through barter. He had a reputation for "reading" children's heads, through the contours being able to tell the parents to what occupation the children were adapted. How this would stack up against modern aptitude tests is not known. All in all, Sandy was a super salesman and did a great deal to publicize and distribute the McIntosh apple.

Allan's youngest son, Harvey (1863–1940), was the one to continue the nursery business. With only an inherited 50 acres of land, Harvey found it necessary, to keep supply up to demand, to arrange for the growing of nursery trees on other farms of the district. Each winter, Harvey McIntosh had four or five men hired to make grafts for planting the following spring. Early each year he sent out cards to prospective customers indicating a nearby sales point with date of being there. He reached these retail stations by horse-drawn wagon. Often he had to sell his trees on credit.

Harvey's only son, Allan, took over his father's business after his death in 1940 but the nursery became much less important than the orchard, about 75 acres mostly of the McIntosh variety.

The original McIntosh tree was only 15 feet away from the McIntosh house. When the house burned down in 1894 the tree was nearly lost (Fig. 1). Allan made desperate efforts to save it from the flames and soon afterwards did some repair work on

FIG. 1.   The original McIntosh tree as it looked in 1896. Fire, which burned
down the nearby house in 1894, badly damaged the trunk. The tree
broke off in 1910. Allan McIntosh, son of the discoverer, stands
beside the tree.
(Courtesy, Canadian Department of Agriculture, Ottawa)

the wounded side. However, the scorching weakened the tree so much that it never regained its vigor of growth. Its last harvest was in 1908 and two years later the tree fell over at the ripe old age of about 100 years. (Memorial, Fig. 2) By this time there were thousands of its kind scattered throughout Eastern North America.

## SALIENT CHARACTERISTICS

McIntosh is an annual bearer with some tendency to alternating heavy and light crops. It has the very desirable quality of thinning its crop without the aid of hormone sprays. The tree is very large and spreading. Seldom does it break down from weak crotches. McIntosh has a reputation for scab susceptibility but ordinarily an adequate spray program will reduce it to negligible amounts. Only in years of long continued warm wet periods in the spring will it be a serious problem. The nitrogen level in the tree must not be too high else color is poor and preharvest drop is worse, but, timely hormone sprays furnish good control of dropping. However, if left on the tree beyond optimum maturity, storage life is sacrificed. Under good conditions, the fruits will keep in cold and CA storage to April and June respectively. McIntosh is primarily a dessert apple but well matured fruits make good sauce and juice. By a special process developed at the Products Laboratory at Vineland, Ontario, canned slices make excellent pies.

## THOUGHTS ON ORIGIN OF McINTOSH

The parentage of McIntosh has been the subject of much speculation. Beach in *Apples of New York* (Vol. 1, p. 25, 1905) places McIntosh in the Fameuse group with that variety, Canada Baldwin, Louise, Scarlet Pippin, and Shiawassee. Of these, only Fameuse itself was old enough to be a parent of McIntosh and yet experience with Fameuse as a parent has been disappointing at Vineland and elsewhere. Could one of the

Fig. 2. Memorial erected to the original McIntosh tree, Dundela, Dundas County, Ontario. The tree stood about 20 rods north of this spot. (Courtesy, Canadian Department of Agriculture, Ottawa)

parents have been Fall St. Lawrence? Beach says St. Lawrence was recommended in England in 1835 and that it probably originated in Quebec Province. It is quite likely, therefore, that St. Lawrence was also old enough to be a parent of McIntosh. St. Lawrence is so nearly like Fameuse in vegetative characters and susceptibility to scab that it is probably a seedling of that variety. There is no record of St. Lawrence being used in breeding work so its potential is not known.

Since all apple varieties are essentially self-unfruitful, there must have been another parent of McIntosh. This is even more speculative than the first parent. Alexander is a possibility because of its similarity in foliage characters to McIntosh. It is an old Russian variety which was known in Canada at the time of McIntosh's infancy. That it transmits McIntosh vegetative characters to its offspring is shown by its seedling Wolf River which Dr. Shaw of Massachusetts found badly intermixed with McIntosh in New England nurseries in the early 1920's. If Fall St. Lawrence and Alexander were the parents of McIntosh, the latter's winter hardiness could be understood but scarcely its high eating quality. But quality might be an inheritance from further back in its ancestry. Even if McIntosh's parents were definitely known, a repetition of the cross would not necessarily assure a line of McIntosh-like apples.

## STRAINS

Most authorities agree that the original McIntosh was a blush-type apple. The much less desirable streak type began to show up in commercial orchards about 1930. Close examination in orchards showed whole trees and parts of trees bearing fruits of the streak type. There seemed to be rather free sporting to this less desirable strain. Conversely, no sporting from the streak type to the blush type was found. Orchards which had come into bearing previous to 1930 were free of the streak type, or almost so. Why the McIntosh suddenly began to sport to the streak type is a puzzle.

Experiment Station workers and nurseries began in the early 30's to select good blush types of McIntosh for propagation. The Ontario Horticultural Experiment Station, for instance, got buds from a selected tree in the W.L. Hamilton orchard near Collingwood. Apples from this orchard had consistently won prizes at the Toronto Royal Winter Fair for good color and general excellence. A stock of this strain was worked up and many thousands of buds were distributed to Ontario nurseries. Unfortunately this strain proved to be unstable in color, about 10% of the trees therefrom being wholly or partly of the streak type. Some authorities now believe they have uncovered strains which are stable vegetatively for blush color. Just because a tree bears 100% blush-type fruit does not seem to assure that propagations from it are free from the streak type of fruit. Some trees are probably wholly stable for color of fruit, others are not. The problem for nurseries is to find the stable ones. In these days of intense competition for markets, growers cannot afford to have even a small proportion of the streak type of McIntosh. It is much less attractive and lowers the inspection grade. Blodgett and Aichele (Wash. Hort. Bull. No. 3, 1960) list 7 red sports of McIntosh, one of which is classed as spur type.

Dr. D.V. Fisher of the Summerland, B.C. Research Station reports (American Fruit Grower 89 (11): 12-14, 16. 1969) the finding of five spur type McIntosh sports in British Columbia. Four of them are being propagated by nurseries in United States and Canada but, at that time, only one had been named—Mac Spur. One of the five is a limb sport at a pruning cut at the top of a 50 year old tree; the others are whole tree sports. All seem to be more resistant to powdery mildew than the standard McIntosh but in some of them there is a tendency to short stems and oblate shape in the fruits. One of the sports seems to have added resistance to spring frost. Pollen of one sport used on Golden Delicious has given nearly 50% spur type among the seedlings.

## CLIMATE FOR McINTOSH

It is hard to beat the McIntosh as it grows near its place of origin, the upper St. Lawrence Valley. In Ontario, the Georgian Bay area produces apples close in quality to the "home" district. McIntosh is also a very satisfactory variety in Quebec, Nova Scotia, Northern Michigan, New York, the New England States, and in British Columbia. Further south it becomes a fall apple, not a winter one, is softer, poor in color, and drops before it attains good quality. McIntosh is a northern variety requiring bright days but cool nights for good color and quality.

## McINTOSH AS A PARENT

There are three research findings which have helped to place McIntosh in its pre-eminent position in Northeastern North America—control of scab by fungicides, reduction in preharvest drop through hormone sprays, and the extension of storage life in controlled atmospheres. All of these characteristics represented points of weakness in its armor. Put alongside its annual cropping character, its high yield, its attractiveness, and its quality, these developments have assured McIntosh a large place in apple breeding programs. For example, Canada Department of Agriculture named Melba (McIntosh open-pollinated) in 1909 and the New York Station named Cortland (Ben Davis x McIntosh) in 1915. Both Stations have continued to use McIntosh and have named many other selections from McIntosh breeding (Table 1).

All of the named hybrids of McIntosh bear unmistakable McIntosh leaf and other vegetative characters. Without being aware of the parentage, a person knowing leaf characters of varieties would say at once that these varieties carried McIntosh "blood". Cortland, for instance, has a typical McIntosh leaf but lacks the heart-shaped leaf base of the parent. In a general

TABLE 1.  New varieties with McIntosh as one of the parents

1.  Canada Department of Agriculture, Ottawa

| | | |
|---|---|---|
| Bancroft | (Forest x McIntosh) | —1930 |
| Edgar | (McIntosh x Forest) | —1929 |
| Hume | (McIntosh open-pollinated) | —1916 |
| Joyce | (McIntosh open-pollinated) | —1912 |
| *Jubilee | (McIntosh x Grimes Golden) | —1939 |
| Lobo | (McIntosh open-pollinated) | —1910 |
| Melba | (McIntosh open-pollinated) | —1909 |
| Newtosh | (McIntosh x Yellow Newtown) | —1922 |
| *Spartan | (McIntosh x Yellow Newtown) | —1936 |
| *Spencer | (McIntosh x Golden Delicious) | —1959 |
| *Summerred (McIntosh x Golden Delicious) x OPEN | | —1964 |
| *Summerland, B.C. Station | | |

2.  Agriculrural Experiment Station, Geneva, N.Y.

| | | |
|---|---|---|
| Barry | (McIntosh x Cox Orange) | —1957 |
| Cortland | (Ben Davis x McIntosh) | —1915 |
| Early McIntosh (Yellow Transparent x McIntosh) | | —1923 |
| Empire | (McIntosh x Delicious) | —1966 |
| Greendale | (McIntosh x Lodi) | —1938 |
| Kendall | (Zusoff x McIntosh) | —1932 |
| Macoun | (McIntosh x Jersey Black) | —1923 |
| Milton | (Yellow Transparent x McIntosh) | —1923 |
| Niagara | (Carlton x McIntosh) | —1962 |
| Ogden | (Zusoff x McIntosh) | —1928 |
| Onondaga | (Ben Davis x McIntosh) | —1915 |
| Otsego | (Ben Davis x McIntosh) | —1914 |
| Redhook | (McIntosh x Carlton) | —1938 |
| Sweet McIntosh (Lawver x McIntosh) | | —1922 |

3.  Other Stations

| | | |
|---|---|---|
| Kyokko | (Ralls Janet x McIntosh, Japan) | —1931 |
| Merton Charm (McIntosh x Cox Orange, England) | | —1933 |
| Michaelmas Red (McIntosh x Worcester Pearmain, England) | | —1929 |
| Puritan | (McIntosh x Red Astrachan, Massachusetts) | —1953 |
| Tydeman's Red (Worcester Pearmain x McIntosh, England) | | —1945 |

way the leaves of all of the named hybrids of McIntosh show the yellow pigment characteristic of the McIntosh variety.

## McINTOSH DESCENDANTS

As already indicated, McIntosh has been freely used in breeding work, and has given some noteworthy hybrids, but thus far they are not close rivals of their famous parent. In order of their age, a few of the most important ones are here discussed with particular relation to their acceptance in different parts of the continent.

*Melba.* The male parent of this variety is not known but it may very well have been a hardier variety than McIntosh—and Ottawa had a good collection in this category. Anyway, it is generally agreed that it is even hardier than McIntosh. It has never attained much prominence in United States but in Quebec and New Brunswick it is in fourth position among varieties, and sixth in Ontario. In 1963, 6% of all apple trees in Quebec were of this variety; in 1959, 3% of New Brunswick's trees were Melba; and in 1966, Ontario's Melbas were over 2% of the total.

Unlike its female parent, sporting in skin color has been rare in Melba. One red sport is being propagated rather freely now under the name of Red Melba. G.H. Dickson recorded its history and characteristics in the 1959-60 Report of the Ontario Horticultural Experiment Station. It has blush color rather than the typical streak of the original Melba. It is slightly later in maturing, is firmer, but, even more important, bruising is not as conspicuous as on the streak type.

*Lobo.* This variety has never attained much prominence except in New Brunswick and Quebec where it ranks in third and fifth place respectively. Even in these provinces, it represents only 4 and 5% of the total apple trees. It is not as good quality as McIntosh and does not store as well, but it is a few days earlier which often means reasonably good prices if sold from the tree.

Lobo has been more satisfactory than McIntosh in the middle Atlantic States.

*Cortland.* Cortland has assumed importance only in the Northeastern States and Provinces which can be shown best by the following table:

| Region | Position among varieties | % of total trees |
|--------|--------------------------|------------------|
| New Brunswick | 2nd | 19 |
| Quebec | 2nd | 7 |
| Ontario | 5th | 3 |
| New York | 5th | 8 |
| Nova Scotia | 6th | 7 |

Cortland lacks the bright color and high aroma of McIntosh, but it has size and is excellent for baking and for salads. Attempts to induce color sporting through irradiation have not been very successful in Nova Scotia nor have natural sports been any improvement.

*Early McIntosh.* For an early apple, about 5 weeks ahead of McIntosh, this variety has good quality. Its main weakness is lack of size. Being decidedly biennial in bearing, an extremely good thinning job is required in order to get adequate fruit-size. About 2% of the apple trees in Ontario and 1% in New York are of this variety. In 1966, it was in eighth position in Ontario.

*Spartan.* Spartan has assumed importance mainly in its place of origin, viz., the Okanagan Valley of British Columbia. Here in 1964, it made up 17% of all apple trees which gave it third position. In that same year, it was reported as 1% of the plantings in Nova Scotia. In the eastern areas, where irrigation is seldom used for apples, the fruits often lack size.

*Tydeman's Red.* The original name, (Tydeman's Early Worcester) given in England, its place of origin, is not used in North America partly because of its length, but also because it is misleading: other varieties mature as much as five weeks earlier in North America. In Ontario, it is ready to pick about 11 days after Early McIntosh. Since it colors very early, there is a real danger of picking it immature with resultant very poor quality. It is a very firm apple and should ship well. Two or more pickings are required. Recently this variety has been extensively planted in British Columbia. There, the trees tend to become "willowy" against which special pruning methods are recommended.

*Puritan.* Puritan matures in Melba season, has medium size, dark red color, and good quality. Like its male parent, Red Astrachan, the flesh is fairly acid. It tends to the biennial bearing habit, and requires two or more pickings. Sauce made from this variety has not had a high rating at Vineland.

## DISTRIBUTION OF McINTOSH TREES

In 1965 there appeared to be well over 3 million McIntosh trees in orchards in North America. It is the leading variety in the Northeastern United States and in Eastern Canada and is an important part of the apple industry in the Province of British Columbia on the other side of the continent. Variety surveys in various States and Provinces have been taken within the past 10 years. McIntosh populations are here given by States and Provinces in apparent order of decreasing number of trees, standards and dwarfs, in commercial orchards (to nearest thousand).

*Quebec.* In 1963, Quebec reported 715,000 McIntosh trees of all ages which was 62% of all apple trees. Sixteen per cent of the trees were under 6 years of age.

*New York.* In 1962 New York had 681,000 trees of all ages of which 16% were nonbearing. About 2/3 of the total was in the Eastern part of the State.

*Ontario.* In 1966 there were 440,000 McIntosh trees in Ontario orchards, 28% of which were nonbearing. This is a considerable increase over the 315,000 reported in 1956. In the 1966 census, 1/3 of the trees were on dwarfing rootstocks.

*Michigan.* In 1962, Michigan orchards had 335,000 bearing trees and about ¼ that number of nonbearing trees. In 1945, Michigan had 440,000 bearing trees but, with per tree yields rising in the interval, it is unlikely that there was less production in 1962 than in 1945. The 1968 production of McIntosh in Michigan was 2,830,000 bushels.

*British Columbia.* In 1955 British Columbia had 333,000 McIntosh trees of all ages; in 1960, 344,000 trees; and in 1964, 381,000 trees, about 1/3 of them under 6 years. Of 100,000 trees planted from 1956 to 1960, 56,000 were on Malling and Malling-Merton rootstocks. McIntosh follows Red Delicious in number of trees.

*Massachusetts.* Unfortunately there is no information on numbers of trees since the 1955 survey when there were 167,000 of all ages of which 12.5% were nonbearing. In 1925 there were 235,000 and in 1940, 376,000. In spite of declining tree numbers, storage holdings of McIntosh have gone from 698,000 bu. per year 1934-43, to 930,000 bu. 1944-53, and to 1,284,000 bu. 1954-63. A large part of these increases is likely due to increasing yield per tree resulting from better cultural methods and this holds also for other areas in North America. Dr. William J. Lord, Extension Pomologist for the State, says "McIntosh is the variety that keeps New England in the apple business."

*Maine.* Again the most recent count of trees was in 1955 when 95,000 McIntosh were reported. It is estimated that about 50,-000 have been planted since that time. From 60 to 70% of new plantings are of the McIntosh variety.

*Wisconsin.* Using acreage and percentage (30) McIntosh figures supplied by the Fruit Extension Specialist in the State, it appears that in 1964 there were about 120,000 McIntosh trees of all ages in commercial orchards in Wisconsin.

*Nova Scotia.* Total number of McIntosh trees in Nova Scotia in 1964 was 108,000. Over 1/3 of them were under 5 years of age so it is to be expected that production in this Province will rise rapidly in the next few years.

*Vermont.* The most recent survey in Vermont included plantings of 1956. There were 78,000 bearing trees and 7,000 nonbearing trees of McIntosh, 64% of trees of all ages. It is estimated that plantings since 1956 are running over 70% McIntosh.

*New Hampshire.* New Hampshire and Vermont are probably very close in total numbers of McIntosh trees. A 1963 survey in New Hampshire gives 92,000 McIntosh trees of all ages. In another 10 years it is estimated that the McIntosh crop will go from the present 1 million bushels to 1½ million.

*New Brunswick.* There has been no apple variety census since 1959. At that time, there were 65,000 McIntosh trees of all ages, only 4% of which were in the 1-5 year age group. However, nearly half of the apple trees in New Brunswick are of the McIntosh variety.

*Connecticut.* No survey of tree numbers is available for Connecticut. On Nov. 1, 1964 there were 440,000 bu. of this variety in storage. This might represent the crop from 40,000-50,000 trees. It is anticipated that there will be little, if any, increase in McIntosh production in the next few years.

# VIII. NORTHERN SPY*

## W.H. UPSHALL
### Director *(retired)*,

Horticultural Experiment Station,
Vineland Station, Ontario

EVEN BEFORE JOHNNY APPLESEED COMMENCED SOWING AP-
ple seeds in Ohio and Indiana (1801-1847), the Chapin family
were planting them on their farms in Ontario County, New
York. Oliver Chapin came from Salisbury, Conn. in 1789,
bought Lot 17 (300 acres), two miles north of East Bloomfield
from Captain William Bacon for 45 pounds sterling. That fall he
went back to Salisbury but returned in the spring (1790) accom-
panied by his brother, Dr. Daniel Chapin, Aaron Taylor, and
their families. It is recorded that Dr. Chapin brought apple
seeds with him at that time and sowed them the same spring,
probably on his brother's farm. In any case, there were 50 acres
of orchard derived from this seed on Oliver's farm when he died
in 1822. In 1876 a portion of these trees still remained, some
having a trunk diameter of three feet. Dr. Daniel Chapin prac-
ticed medicine in East Bloomfield until 1807 when he moved
to Buffalo, where he continued his work until his death in 1821.

Six years after Dr. Chapin's arrival in New York State, another brother, Heman, came from Connecticut. Four years later
(1800) he bought 2/3 of Lot 19 second to the west of his brother
Oliver. He was 22 years old at the time. Whether he brought a

*The writer is indebted to Mr. J. Sheldon Fisher, Ontario County (N.Y.), Historian,
Valentown Hall, Fishers for information about the originators. Much other information
on the variety has been obtained from *Abstract Bibliography of Fruit Breeding and
Genetics to 1960, Malus and Pyrus*, by R.L. Knight.

new lot of apple seed with him from Connecticut or used some of the seedlings derived from his brother Daniel's planting is not known. However, he is given credit for originating the Northern Spy and also two other varieties, Early Joe and Melon, neither of which have achieved the fame of Northern Spy and are now almost unknown. At this early time, grafted trees were unknown necessitating the use of seedlings from trees bearing superior fruit.

An interesting aspect of the story is that the original Northern Spy tree never bore fruit. It died before reaching the fruiting stage. However, it had thrown up some vigorous suckers from the root before its demise and Roswell Humphrey, a brother-in-law of Heman, whose farm was immediately to the north (Lot 6), had planted them in his own orchard. Here they fruited and in the course of time established a reputation for eating quality, for long storage, and for processing excellence.

Heman Chapin was an Assemblyman for one term. He married Electa Humphrey (sister of Roswell) and they had three sons and five daughters. His son, Oliver C., took over the home farm in due course as did his grandson, Harry G., at a later time. In 1893 Harry G. Chapin was the owner of the farm. When his father died in 1881 there were 135 acres of orchard on the place with production running as high as 10,000 barrels per year. What proportion of this planting was of the Northern Spy variety is not recorded. The Chapin farm remained in the family for over 100 years but both this farm and the Humphrey one have now (1965) passed to other families—and no orchard remains on either of them.

It was not until about 1840 that Northern Spy became known outside its neighborhood of origin. In 1852 the American Pomological Society recommended it for general planting. Many years ago a concrete marker was placed near the point of origin of the variety and, as if to prove that Northern Spy would still thrive in its place of birth, a tree was planted near the marker on April 12, 1964 (Fig. 1 and 2). On that occasion officials of historical societies, the apple industry, and government were present to pay tribute to a variety which had found a place in New York State and beyond. The marker is situated on the south side of Boughton Road about 1/10 mile west of County Road 3 running from Holcomb to Victor.

## SALIENT FEATURES

Northern Spy is notoriously late in coming into bearing. The tree is very upright in habit in its early years but, with a bare minimum of pruning after the training process is completed, it comes into bearing earlier. These early crops pull the tree into a more desirable shape. The use of dwarfing and semidwarfing rootstocks, by inducing earlier bearing, also give improved tree form. Spy blooms later in the spring than most other varieties but there is sufficient overlap with all the midseason bloomers such as McIntosh, Delicious, and Golden Delicious. The fruit itself is essentially streaked with bright red color but some blushed-type sports are available. In Michigan, New York, and Ontario it is almost the last variety to be picked, so late in fact that some years the fruits may get frosted slightly. However, if not handled until they thaw out no harm is done. The fruits bruise very easily and must be handled with great care at all times if a first grade product is to be offered for sale. Spies store well both in cold and CA storage, remaining in good condition until May and July respectively.

## BUD SPORTS

It was not until Starking, a red sport of Delicious, was discovered in 1921 that growers and others began to keep their eyes open for whole tree and limb sports of all apple varieties. For nearly 100 years no sports of Northern Spy had been reported. That they were not present is very unlikely. By 1933, Bregger had reported to the American Society for Horticultural Science the presence of 13 for this one variety. One of them was the Red Spy which was found on the farm of William C. Greene, Victor, N.Y. about 1895. It was distributed by the N.Y. Fruit Testing

Association from 1923 to 1954. Another was Redwin Spy which was discovered near Paris, Ontario about 1930. Some of the Spy sports are blush type, others streaked type, the latter generally preferred. The Geneva, N.Y. Station rated 10 red types in 1964 and the Greene and Redwin sports were low in attractiveness.

Unlike the Delicious sports, the strains of Red Spy have never become very popular. Markets did not recognize them as Spy apples for the trade was accustomed to a green and red striped apple. There were reports of poor storage behavior for the Spy sports and Clarke of the Pennsylvania Station made this fact official in a report to the American Society for Horticultural Science in 1952. Also, as early as 1931, Drain had reported to the Maine Pomological Society that some strains of Red Spy lacked vigor.

In 1961, Red Spy trees in Ontario were 14% of the total Spy trees. Most of them were planted between 1930 and 1945. Growers are now (1965) showing a preference for Northern Spy over its sports. In New York State, Red Spy trees are estimated at less than 5% of total Spy trees.

## HARDINESS

It is generally considered that Northern Spy trees are relatively tender to winter cold. Long continued growth and late leaf fall may be contributing factors. Sandsten of Colorado reported in 1924 that N. Spy trees were among others that were dead after 10 years in the orchard. Blair of Ottawa, Canada, after the severe winter of 1933-34 rated Spy injury as 89 with Duchess (hardy) at 5 and Delicious (tender) at 100. After that same winter, Waring and Hilborn of Maine put Spy in the "definitely tender" group. After a November, 1940 freeze, Pickett and Lantz of Iowa placed Spy in the second worst injured group (out of 6). After an earlier severe winter, Oskamp of Indiana put Spy in the "most injured" group but Shaw of Massachusetts reported Spy rarely injured in the same year, while

Baldwin, R.I. Greening, Gravenstein, and King were severely injured. Results in Ontario after the 1933-34 winter were similar to those reported by Shaw earlier. Many Baldwin and R.I. Greening trees did not survive, particularly trees which had borne heavy crops in 1933. Very few Spy trees were lost at this time. On the basis of all records, it is probably correct to say that the hardiness of Spy lies somewhere between McIntosh and R.I. Greening (or Baldwin). Because Spy is very late in blossoming in the spring, the bloom may escape the frosts which damage earlier blossoming varieties.

## SPY AS A PROCESSOR

Spy is recognized in Ontario, Michigan, and New York as an excellent processor—for sauce, frozen apple slices for pies, and for juice. It is not noted for whole-apple baking. A writer for the New York Horticultural Society said in 1964 "Processors pay a higher price for Northern Spy for apple slices than for any other variety." Since the variety stores well, it gives a long season for processing. Processors are often unable to get supplies of Spy because it is in demand for fresh sales to consumers at a price higher than the processors care to pay. However, Spy often bears poorly colored apples on the lower heavily shaded limbs and in the interior of the tree. Because of their lack of color they are graded down and therefore bring less money on the fresh market. These apples are quite acceptable to processors for the skins are discarded anyway.

Spy is noted for its high content of Vitamin C. In the fresh state, it has about 4 times as much as McIntosh. However, a high proportion of Vitamin C is lost in commercial processing.

## SPY AS A ROOTSTOCK

In countries where feeding by woolly aphis *(Eriosoma lanigera)* has weakened both nursery and orchard apple trees, clonal

Spy rootstocks have been used successfully for many years. Their history in Australia goes back to 1890 and probably nearly as far in New Zealand and South Africa. It is one of the very few apple varieties immune, or nearly so, to this persistent pest. Because it was used so widely in the foregoing countries, Hatton of the East Malling Research Station, England compared it with a number of Malling clones and concluded in 1927 that it was a semidwarfing rootstock but not superior to Malling I and II for English conditions. There, woolly aphis was not a serious pest. Later (1936), Miss Hearman of Australia after numerous excavations at East Malling concluded that the root system of Spy was weak, often one-sided, and with little fibre. It was adversely affected by drouth and competition from other roots.

More recently (1963) Cole of Australia, after a survey of apple orchards in several northern and southern hemisphere countries, says "My observations suggest, however, that our Northern Spy rootstock should not be discarded lightly." He mentions the problem of poor anchorage under some conditions and the need for virus-free lines. McKenzie of New Zealand in a 1964 report also speaks well of Spy as a rootstock. He says, "Where a rootstock of moderate vigor is required, Northern Spy appears to be the best selection. It is highly resistant to woolly aphid and is an excellent nursery rootstock."

The Malling-Merton (MM) series of apple rootstocks, now extensively used throughout the world, are from crosses with Spy. The idea was to get resistance to woolly aphis in addition to other desirable characters. Perhaps in the course of time one or more of them may replace the parent in the "woolly aphis" countries. The more interesting ones at the moment, with parentages, are

MM 106—N. Spy x M 1
MM 104—M II x N. Spy
MM 111—N. Spy x Merton 793 (N. Spy x M II)

## SPY AS A PARENT

The Ontario variety is the best known seedling of Northern Spy. The male parent was Wagener. Charles Arnold of Paris, Ontario made the cross and the resulting variety was described first in 1874. Early in the 20th century it was planted fairly extensively in Ontario as a good processor, late keeper, of possible value. It was never in a quality class with Spy and unfortunately it became mixed with that variety in several Ontario nurseries much to the chagrin of orchardists who planted the mixture. The Ontario variety has achieved some importance in parts of Europe but it is now hard to find in North America.

Northern Spy and some of its red sports have been used in breeding work in Iowa, New York, Ohio, and Ontario. Also, the Canada Department of Agriculture at Ottawa has used Spy extensively as a parent. Generally, it is agreed that Spy transmits size, better than average quality, good flesh characters, moderate acid, late-season blossoming, late harvest, but not wood hardiness.

From 1910 to 1930 the Ottawa Station named 38 selections (Table 1) out of Spy seedlings, all but one open-pollinated. None has achieved any commercial importance in Ontario or elsewhere and are unlikely to do so now. The nearest to fame is probably Sandow in New Brunswick (Canada) where in 1959 it was 1.5% of apple trees of all ages.

The New York (Geneva) Station has named 6 Spy selections (Table 1), 3 of them in 1914 and 1915 which are unlikely to be planted again. Spigold and Wayne were named in 1962 and Spijon in 1968. It is much too soon to give them a commercial rating.

## SPY 227

In 1923 Yerkes of USDA Arlington, Va. Farm saved open-pollinated seed of N. Spy from a variety orchard. One of them, 227, proved to have exceptional vigor, was highly resistant to woolly aphis, and easy to propagate by root cuttings. This root-

Table 1. New varieties with Spy as one of the parents

1.  Canada Department of Agriculture

| | | | | |
|---|---|---|---|---|
| Ascot | (Northern Spy open-pollinated) | | | — 1913 |
| Bingo | ,, | ,, | ,, | — 1911 |
| Currie | ,, | ,, | ,, | — 1920 |
| Donald | ,, | ,, | ,, | — 1912 |
| Elmer | ,, | ,, | ,, | — 1912 |
| Emilia | ,, | ,, | ,, | — 1915 |
| Epsom | ,, | ,, | ,, | — 1913 |
| Galton | ,, | ,, | ,, | — 1915 |
| Glenton | ,, | ,, | ,, | — 1911 |
| Homer | ,, | ,, | ,, | — 1910 |
| Lipton | ,, | ,, | ,, | — 1915 |
| Marcus | ,, | ,, | ,, | — 1912 |
| Margery | (Pioneer x Northern Spy) | | | — 1911 |
| Marne | (Northern Spy open-pollinated) | | | — 1915 |
| Nestor | ,, | ,, | ,, | — 1912 |
| Niobe | ,, | ,, | ,, | — 1911 |
| Orlando | ,, | ,, | ,, | — 1913 |
| Pandora | ,, | ,, | ,, | — 1913 |
| Rocket | ,, | ,, | ,, | — 1911 |
| Rosalie | ,, | ,, | ,, | — 1911 |
| Sandow | ,, | ,, | ,, | — 1912 |
| Sparta | ,, | ,, | ,, | — 1914 |
| Spiana | ,, | ,, | ,, | — 1925 |
| Spicap | ,, | ,, | ,, | — 1929 |
| Spiland | ,, | ,, | ,, | — 1923 |
| Spikee | ,, | ,, | ,, | — 1926 |
| Spiman | ,, | ,, | ,, | — 1929 |
| Spimil | ,, | ,, | ,, | — 1922 |
| Spimore | ,, | ,, | ,, | — 1923 |
| Spiotta | ,, | ,, | ,, | — 1920 |
| Spiretta | ,, | ,, | ,, | — 1923 |
| Spiro | ,, | ,, | ,, | — 1920 |
| Spitone | ,, | ,, | ,, | — 1930 |
| Spiwell | ,, | ,, | ,, | — 1927 |
| Spiza | ,, | ,, | ,, | — 1922 |

| Tasty | " | " | " | — 1912 |
| Thurso | " | " | " | — 1908 |
| Wilgar | " | " | " | — 1923 |

2. Agricultural Experiment Station, Geneva, N.Y.

| | |
|---|---|
| Oswego (Sutton x Northern Spy) | — 1915 |
| Schoharie (Ralls x Northern Spy) | — 1914 |
| Spigold (Red Spy x Golden Delicious) | — 1962 |
| Spijon (Red Spy x Monroe) | — 1968 |
| Tioga (Sutton x Northern Spy) | — 1915 |
| Wayne (N.W. Greening x Red Spy) | — 1962 |

stock was distributed to the New York and Massachusetts Stations for trials with several varieties. At both Stations, some scion varieties gave weak budlings which died when the tops became two and three years old. The puzzling thing was that some bud sources of a certain variety gave healthy trees and others gave weak trees which soon died. The younger roots died first, then the older roots, followed by trunk and branches. It is of interest that N. Spy on Spy 227 was unsuccessful for the USDA but gave no trouble at the New York Station.

At first, the theory was advanced that the results could be explained by somatic variation, i.e., strains, within the apple varieties. It is now agreed, however, that Spy 227 is a very sensitive indicator of one or more viruses, perhaps a complex. Virologists are not yet sure what viruses are involved in this case but it appears that there is some relation to the stempitting virus. It is an interesting situation where a selection did not prove successful as a rootstock but has found another use which may turn out to be just as valuable.

## DISTRIBUTION OF SPY TREES

In order to maintain production, it has been estimated that about 10% of the trees of any apple variety must be in the nonbearing class. It may be said for some areas that production

will decline for Spy and its sports. They are Maine, New Hampshire, Quebec, and Vermont, none of which was very important
in Spy production at any time. The variety is borderline in
hardiness for these areas. The numbers of trees of all ages for
most recent census, in parentheses, was—Vermont (1957),
15000; Maine (1955), 12000; Massachusetts (1955), 9000;
Quebec (1963), 3000; New Hampshire (1963), 2000. It appears
that in Michigan, New York and Ontario production of Spy will
remain more or less static in the next few years. Nova Scotia
is the only area which is likely to have increased production.
These latter four areas, in which Spy is still an important variety, will be discussed separately.

An educated guess is that there are now about 680,000 Spy
trees of all ages and all sports in the above areas. This is probably a very high percentage of the totals for Canada and United
States.

*Michigan.* The number of bearing Spy trees (8 year and over)
in Michigan has gone down continuously since 1945 as here
indicated.

$$1945 — 385,000$$
$$1950 — 345,000$$
$$1955 — 300,000$$
$$1960 — 255,000$$
$$1962 — 225,000$$

However, it is estimated that there were in 1962 an additional
10% of nonbearing trees which would probably be enough to
maintain production at the 1962 level. It is very likely that a fair
percentage of the nonbearing trees are on dwarfing rootstocks
and will come into bearing sooner than standards.

*Ontario.* Spy trees of all ages and on all rootstocks in four
surveys were as follows:

1941 — 246,000
1956 — 210,000
1961 — 240,000
1966 — 240,000

In spite of the planting of 10,000 Spy trees on dwarfing root-stocks from 1941 to 1956, there was still a considerable drop in total trees. Largely due to heavy plantings of dwarfs (30,000 from 1956 to 1961), the Spy population rose in that period. The dwarfs were on Malling VII, IX, and II in descending order. Undoubtedly the aim of the grower was to get earlier production with this late-bearing variety, increased yields per acre in the early years, and more economical handling in spraying, thinning, and picking. From 1961 to 1966, new plantings of Spy had just balanced removals.

*New York.* In 1962 New York had about 100,000 Spy trees of all ages, and on all rootstocks. There appears to be no data on proportion of trees on dwarfing rootstocks. It has been estimated in 1962 that about 10% of the total were nonbearing. This should be enough to maintain production at the 1962 level for a few years.

*Nova Scotia.* Nova Scotia's trend in Spy population is similar to Ontario's (see above) but is even more spectacular in recent years. In the 1-5 year bracket there were, in 1964, 26% of the trees of all ages. This indicates a fair increase in production in the next few years. The fact that Nova Scotia has convenient processing plants has probably influenced decisions to plant Spy. There is no separate record for Spy with respect to division by rootstock but for all varieties in the survey under five years about 50% were on clonal rootstocks, mostly dwarfing.

1949 — 80,000
1959 — 43,000
1964 — 59,000

**OUTLOOK FOR SPY**

Spy has several attributes in favor of it. It is a good dessert apple and also a good processor and this is true of few apple varieties. Its late season blooming sometimes lets it get by a spring frost. On the other side of the ledger it is late coming into bearing, tends to be biennial in bearing, forms tree crotches which break easily, and the fruit is easily bruised. With the exception of the last fault, with improved methods of culture some measure of control should be possible. One of these days, someone may find, or produce, a spur type Spy giving much smaller trees even on well anchored rootstocks. Another possibility is the dwarfing of Spy with growth retarding chemicals.

FIG. 1.  Right, Northern Spy marker; left, Dr. Roger Way, Experiment Station, Geneva, N.Y. beside Northern Spy tree planted during the 1964 Ceremony. Picture taken Nov. 1965.
(Courtesy, Agr. Exp. Station, Geveva, N.Y.)

FIG. 2.  The plaque on the Northern Spy marker.
(Courtesy, Agr. Exp. Station, Geneva, N.Y.).

# IX. ROME

## JAMES B. MOWRY

Superintendent of the Illinois Horticultural Experiment Station,
Carbondale, Illinois

THE ROME APPLE IS THE TYPE VARIETY OF AN IMPORTANT
group of varieties originating in and well adapted to the middle
latitudes of commercial apple regions in the United States. The
fruits of Rome and related varieties are generally large, firm,
attractive, and medium in quality. They persistently hang on the
tree at maturity, have a long storage life, and can be successfully
marketed for fresh fruit or culinary uses. Some important tree
characteristics of Rome type varieties are: medium size; up-
right-spreading form; good productivity; annual bearing habit;
late bloom season; late season of maturity; and susceptibility to
apple scab, apple rust, powdery mildew and fire blight.

With few exceptions, Rome and related varieties have a diploid (2n) chromosome constitution. Thus, they have viable
pollen and can be planted as pollinizers for any other variety
whose bloom season adequately overlaps their late season of
bloom. In some locations Rome type varieties may be margin-
ally self-fruitful with self-pollination. However, to insure good
fruit sets in large orchards, they should be interplanted with
another unrelated diploid variety in adequate numbers and
planting designs to insure cross-pollination. Closely related varieties should be suspected of cross-incompatibility.

Within a group of varieties, the order of maturity is fairly
constant, although the actual maturity date may vary in different seasons and with localities. In the following variety descriptions the maturity dates for Rome and related varieties have
been given by calendar date as well as by the number of weeks
before or after the maturity date of Delicious (40).

The comprehensive apple variety displays, promoted by and
shown in conjunction with the annual meetings of the American

Pomological Society, provide an opportunity to evaluate the climatic influences on the attractiveness of apples. Some of these observations by the author have shown that high precipitation during the growing season has a greater adverse effect than high temperature on the attractiveness of Rome apples (40). Rome is better suited to the upper reaches of the Ohio River Valley where it originated, than to more northern or southern regions.

A number of mutations or bud sports have been selected primarily for their ability to produce fruits which develop more intense, more extensive, and more attractive red overcolor than Rome itself. However, a few of them exhibit changes in other characteristics as well as in color. At this time (1969) no spur type sports of Rome have been reported.

## HISTORY AND DESCRIPTION OF ROME*

*Synonyms:* (2) Belle de Rome, Faust's Rome Beauty, Gillett's Seedling, Rome Beauty, Roman Beauty; (43) Press Ewing, Phoenix, Royal Red, Starbuck. Origin: H. N. Gillett, Proctorville, Ohio, Rome Township, Lawrence County. (36) In the fall of 1816 Joel Gillett brought a number of apple trees from Putnam's Nursery, Marietta, Ohio, to a farm two miles above Proctorville, Ohio. While preparing to plant the trees the following spring, he found one which had sprouted from the rootstock below the graft union. This tree was given to his son, Alanson, who planted it in the corner of a field near the Ohio River.

(28) The tree produced such fine apples that it was used for propagation about 1828. The apple was named Rome Beauty by George Walton about 1832; Rome from the name of the township, and Beauty because of the fine appearance. (36) The original tree stood on the bank of the Ohio River until about 1860, when it was undermined and washed away by high waters. H. N. Gillett was largely instrumental in promoting the propaga-

*Throughout the remainder of this article, footnote numbers will preceed the footnoted material.

tion of the new variety. He brought it to the notice of the Ohio Convention of Fruit Growers in 1848.

*Tree.* (2) Standard growth habit; vigorous; young trees upright, later becoming spreading and drooping with slender branches; moderately early bearing; annual bearing habit; productive, sometimes to a fault; diploid with fertile pollen; late bloom season; late season of maturity; (40) 3 weeks after Delicious or October 7 at Carbondale, Ill.; (39) 160–165 days from bloom to maturity; fruit hangs well on the trees at maturity; serious susceptibility to apple scab, apple rust, powdery mildew and fire blight (41).

*Fruit.* (Fig. 1). (2) Large to very large, roundish-oblate to round conic; long, slender stem; cavity smooth and obtuse, no russet. Skin: thick, tough, yellowish-green ground color; 50 to 80% covered with medium red, striped and mottled; lenticels small except in hot, humid summer climates; moderately glossy finish; moderately attractive. Flesh: Yellowish-white, firm to very firm, medium texture, juicy, mildly subacid, medium quality, for

FIG. 1.   Tree-run Rome apples just after picking.
(Courtesy, National Apple Institute)

fresh fruit and culinary uses. Storage life: Long, normally 4 to 5 months to a maximum of 6 or 7 months; fruit condition in cold storage is retained much longer than dessert quality; overmature fruits have dry, mealy, poor quality flesh; immature fruits in storage are subject to serious scald. Controlled atmospheres (CA) give little increase in storage life to Rome and its sports and losses from scald may be increased.

Rome is likely to continue as a profitable variety for commerical fruit growers in the Ohio River Valley because it is very firm at maturity, bears handling exceptionally well, and is adapted to many methods of marketing. The large, firm, regular shaped fruits are well adapted to commercial processing into pie slices and baked apples.

Additional red overcolor, particularly of the blushed type, in bud sports of Rome would be advantageous for marketing, providing the other good qualities of Rome can be retained. The following strains are mutations of Rome or of one of its bud sports. Those which have been patented or commercially propagated are tabulated (Table 1), others are merely listed.

## DESCENDENTS OF ROME

*Anderson.* Synonyms. (23) Paducah; (29) Anderson's Seedling. *Origin:* (29) Herbert Anderson, Kevil, Ky; about 1890. *Parentage:* (29) Open-pollinated seedling of Rome. *Tree:* (29) Resembles Rome, but somewhat more vigorous and upright, productive, early bearing, annual bearing habit; (33) bloom season medium late, about 3 days before Rome; (46) season of maturity about 3 weeks before Rome, (40) with Delicious or about September 15 at Carbondale, Ill.; (39) 134 days from bloom to maturity; (41) moderately resistant to fire blight. *Fruit:* (29) Large, oblate. Skin: yellow ground color, 50% covered with medium red stripes, moderately attractive. Flesh: crisp, juicy, fine grained, good to very good quality.

*Ben Hur. Origin:* (36) Sanford N. Badger, Derby, Ind. *Parentage:* Ben Davis x Rome. *Tree:* Resembles Ben Davis, produc-

TABLE 1. Sports of Rome and of its Mutations

| Name | Origin | | | Color |
|------|--------|--------|--------|-------|
| | Where | When | How | |
| Gallia Beauty[a] (26, 35, 40, 41)[b] | William Coon, Proctorville, Ohio | 1863 | root sprout | blushed |
| Wright (4) | J. H. Wright, Yakima, Wash. | 1902 | whole tree | blushed |
| Double Red (4, 5, 10) | E. E. Cowin, Wapato, Wash. | 1917 | whole trees | blushed striped |
| Ruby (4, 17, 22, 26) | Hall Orchard, Milton-Freewater, Ore. | about 1918 | limb | blushed |
| Clifton (4, 13, 31) | L. J. Clifton Memphis, N.Y. | 1920 | ? | blushed |
| Cox (15, 21, 23, 28) | U. T. Cox Proctorville, Ohio | before 1925 | trunk sprout | blushed |
| H.T.O. (4, 17) | H. T. Bigelow Bangor, Mich. | 1926 | ? | blushed |
| SeeandO No. 262 (4, 5) | Van Husen Orchard, Wenatchee, Wash. | 1927 | limb | blushed striped |
| Barkley (4, 9) | G. L. Barkley Manson, Wash. | 1930 | limb | blushed striped |
| Williams (4, 11, 14) | D. Williams Orchard, Yakima, Wash. | 1931 | whole tree | striped |
| Applegate (4, 12, 41) | L. N. Applegate, Freehold, N. J. | 1935 | whole tree | striped |
| Nero (4, 8, 9) | R. S. Lemcke, Tieton, Wash. | 1948 | whole tree | striped |
| Law (4, 14) | Walter A. Law Tonasket, Wash. | 1952 | limb | blushed |
| Carlson (4, 16) | John Carlson, Yakima, Wash. | 1953 | limb | blushed |
| Summerland | Ward Bros. Kelowna, B. C. | 1956 | limb | blushed |
| Ady (4) | Ady Orchard, Fruitland, Idaho | 1957 | ? | blushed |

[a] Early records on the origin of Gallia Beauty stated that it was a seedling of Rome. However, the facts that the tree is identical to Rome (43) and that it is ineffective as a pollinizer for Rome (37) seem to indicate that it is a sport. It is entirely possible that it arose from a scion root rather than a seedling root.

*References:*

[b] Sports of Rome or its mutants, not sufficiently different from others existing at the time and which were not taken up by a nursery or patented, with references (if any), are as follows: Mills (13), Ohio (18), Sundquist No. 1 (4), Swanson (4), Taylor (4), Baillie, Conical, Dalzell, Frimley, Hotle, Leake, Loop (17, 30), Loop Striped, Magnason, Red (18, 19, 20, 23, 25, 28, 40), Smith, Sundquist No. 2 (4).

tive, early bearer, late bloom season; (40) season of maturity about 4 weeks after Delicious or October 15 at Carbondale, Ill. *Fruit:* Large, roundish oblate. Skin: striped coloring like that of a highly colored Ben Davis. Flesh: white, very firm, juicy, sprightly subacid, good quality. Storage season: longer than Ben Davis and fruit maintains much better quality.

*Crandall.* Synonym. (3) Illinois 1. *Origin:* (3,6) Illinois Agricultural Experiment Station, Urbana, Ill; tree planted in 1914; selected in 1925; named in 1952. *Parentage:* (3,6) Rome x Jonathan. *Tree:* (3) Low spreading, very wide angle crotches, strongly reinforced, moderately vigorous, productive, early bearing, annual bearing habit, medium late bloom season; (40) season of maturity about 4 days after Delicious or about September 20 at Carbondale, Ill.; fruit hangs well at maturity; (41) moderately susceptible to fire blight; (3) less susceptible to apple scab than either parent. *Fruit:* (3, 43, 45, 46) Large, roundish oblate, very firm. Skin: thick, yellow ground color; 50–80% covered with medium red blush, occasionally with indistinct stripes, glossy finish, medium to large lenticels, moderately attractive to attractive. Flesh: yellowish white, fine grained, crisp, juicy, mild subacid, very good quality for dessert or culinary uses. Storage season: (3) very long, February through April or later, best quality reached in late February to mid March well after most varieties have passed their prime; heavy wax prevents drying out and shriveling; no Jonathan or Baldwin spot develops.

*Downing.* *Origin:* (27) Ohio Agricultural Experiment Station, Wooster, Ohio; 1929; named in 1937. *Parentage:* (27) Gallia Beauty x Kirtland. *Tree:* (27) Late bloom season, with Rome; (32) diploid. *Fruit:* (27) Large, roundish oblate, firm. Skin: greenish yellow ground color, dull red blush. Flesh: yellow, moderately coarse and juicy, subacid, good quality; Storage season: to February or March.

*Ensee.* *Origin:* (36) Nelson Cox, Windsor Township, Lawrence County, Ohio; 1880. A chance seedling sprang up near a place where cider had been made in earlier years on the farm of the late Nelson Cox. Little notice was taken of it for several years after it began bearing until 1895, when its crop attracted attention. Since then it has been disseminated in an experimental way, and commercially to a slight extent, by the sons of Mr. Cox. (45) The coined name, Ensee, was applied to the variety about 1898 in perpetuation of the apple brand (N. C.) of the originator, who was for many years recognized as one of the leading commercial apple growers of his region. *Parentage:* Chance seedling. *Tree:* (36) Resembles Rome, young trees upright becoming spreading, moderately vigorous, slender twigs, yellowish bark, bears fruits in terminal clusters, early bearing, biennial bearing habit, late bloom season; season of maturity about 1 week before Rome; fruits hang well at maturity; more susceptible to fire blight than Rome. *Fruit:* (35, 36) Medium to large, roundish oblate, moderately firm, irregularly ribbed. Skin: thin, tough, yellow ground color, orangish red blush and stripes, moderately glossy finish, russets seriously from spray injury, scarf skin moderately attractive. Flesh: yellow, coarse, granular, moderately juicy, rich, subacid, very good quality, Storage season: long, January to March; does not become dry and mealy; susceptible to scald.

*Jerseyred.* Synonym. (9) New Jersey No. 1. *Origin:* (9) New Jersey Agricultural Experiment Station, New Brunswick, N.J.; 1947; named in 1954. *Parentage:* (9) Gallia Beauty x White Winter Pearmain. *Tree:* (1) Triploid, sterile pollen, (41) moderately susceptible to fire blight; (40) season of maturity about 2 weeks later than Rome or about October 20 at Carbondale, Ill. *Fruit:* Very large, round, very firm. Skin: green ground color; 50–80% covered with light red blush, moderately glossy finish, moderately attractive, (9) colors better than Rome in New Jersey; quality better than Rome; long storage, excellent for eating fresh and for cooking.

*Miller Giant. Origin:* (13) Harry Kaiser, Athallia, Ohio found the tree on the farm of Mr. Miller, Union Ridge, Cabell County, W. Va. The tree was planted about 1900 and selected in 1914;

propagated about 1922. *Parentage:* Considered an open-pollinated seedling of Rome. *Tree:* Very vigorous, susceptible to
apple scab, season of maturity 10 days before Rome. *Fruit:*
Large, averaging 16 ounces, with some fruits weighing as much
as 26 ounces and averaging about 3 inches in diameter; quality
similar to Rome and keeps in storage about like Rome.

*Monroe.* Synonym. (5) N.Y. 1546. *Origin:* (5) New York State
Agricultural Experiment Station, Geneva, N.Y.; 1910; selected
in 1921; named in 1949. *Parentage:* (5) Jonathan x Rome. *Tree:*
(5) hardy; annual bearing habit; productive; (40) season of
maturity about 10 days after Delicious or about September 26
at average susceptibility to fire blight, Carbondale, Ill.; (41)
susceptible to powdery mildew. *Fruit:* Round; firm. Skin: yellow ground color, 75% covered with medium red blush, moderately glossy finish, moderately attractive to attractive, medium
size lenticels sensitive to high temperatures and humidity
becoming very prominent from N.J., N.C., and Carbondale, Ill.,
good quality. (5) Storage season: long.

*Roanoke.* (42) Origin. Virginia Polytechnic Institute, Blacksburg, Va., named in 1968. *Parentage:* Rome X Schoharie. *Fruit:*
Matures just before Delicious. Size above average. Skin: excellent bright color and finish. Flesh: firm, aromatic flavor, good
quality. Long storage season.

*Ruby.* Synonyms: (19) not the Ruby originated by Central Experimental Farms, Ottawa, Ont., Canada about 1920. *Origin:*
(7) Ohio Agricultural Experiment Station, Wooster, Ohio;
planted 1935; selected in 1940; named in 1952. *Parentage:* (7)
Gallia Beauty x Starking. *Tree:* (7) Productive, early bearer,
annual bearing habit, late bloom season, (40) season of maturity
with Rome, about 3 weeks after Delicious or October 7 at
Carbondale, Illinois. (41) Average susceptibility to fire blight.
*Fruit:* Large to very large, round conic, firm. Skin: yellowish
green ground color, 80–100% covered with dark red blush
glossy finish, attractive to very attractive. (38) Quality excellent
for cooking, medium for dessert. Storage season: (38) long.

*Warder.* Synonym. (32) Ohio 970. *Origin:* (34) Ohio Agricultural Experiment Station, Wooster, Ohio; (27) planted in 1915; (34) named in 1937. *Parentage:* (5) Open-pollinated seedling of Rome. *Tree:* (5) Resembles Ensee, season of maturity about 1 week before Delicious or September 10 at Carbondale, Ill., (27) late bloom season, with Rome, (32) diploid. *Fruit:* (27) Medium size, roundish oblate. Skin: almost entirely covered and splashed with dark carmine, very attractive. Flesh: white, medium texture, crisp, mild subacid, good quality, (5) dessert quality somewhat better than Rome. Storage season: October to January.

## *Literature Cited*

1. Batra, Shanti, Charlotte Pratt and J. Einset. 1963. Chromosome numbers of apple varieties and sports IV. Proc. Amer. Soc. Hort. Sci., 82: 56–63.
2. Beach, S. A., N. O. Booth and O. M. Taylor, 1905. The apples of New York, N.Y. Agr. Exp. Sta. Rep. 1903. 2 Vol.
3. Birkeland, C. J. and D. F. Dayton. 1951. The Crandall, a new and promising late-keeping apple. Fruit Var. Hort. Dig. 6 (1): 3–4.
4. Blodgett, E. C. and M. D. Aichelle. 1960. Some notes on apple varieties. Wash. State Dept. Agr. Hort. Bull. 3.
5. Brooks, R. M. and H. P. Olmo. 1952. Register of new fruit and nut varieties, 1920–1950. Univ. of Calif. Press. 206 p.
6. Brooks, R. M. and H. P. Olmo. 1952. Register of new fruit and nut varieties. List 7. Proc. Amer. Soc. Hort. Sci. 60: 497–504.
7. _____. 1953. List 8. ibid. 62:513–526.
8. _____. 1954. List 9. ibid. 64:535–549.
9. _____. 1955. List 10. ibid. 66:445–454.
10. _____. 1956. List 11. ibid. 68:611–631.
11. _____. 1957. List 12. ibid. 70:557–584.
12. _____. 1958. List 13. ibid. 72:519–541.
13. _____. 1959. List 14 ibid. 74:758–785.
14. _____. 1960. List 15. ibid. 76:725–758.
15. _____. 1961. List 16. ibid. 78:622–645.
16. _____. 1963. List 18. ibid. 83:862–882.

17. _____. 1964. List 19. ibid. 85:697–724.
18. Clarke, W. S. Jr. and C. M. Ritter. 1955. Apple varieties in central Pennsylvania. Penn. Agr. Exp. Sta. Bull. 605.
19. Close, C. P. (Chairman). 1921. Report of the committee on new fruits and nuts. Proc. Amer. Pomol. Soc. 254.
20. _____. 1923. ibid.: 81.
21. _____. 1925. ibid.: 117.
22. _____. 1928. ibid.: 164.
23. _____. 1930. ibid.: 224, 225.
24. _____. 1932. ibid.: 230.
25. _____. 1933. ibid.: 173, 175.
25. _____. 1933. ibid.: 173, 175.
26. _____. 1934. ibid.: 109, 110.
27. _____. 1938. ibid.: 165.
28. Cox U. T. 1917. The Rome Beauty apple in Ohio. Proc. Amer. Pomol. Soc., 187–189.
29. Darrow, G. 1923. Fruits in West Virginia, Kentucky, and Tennessee. U. S. Dept. Agr. Bull. 1189.
30. Einset, J. and Barbara Imhoff. 1947. Chromosome numbers of apple varieties and sports. Proc. Amer. Soc. Hort. Sci. 50:45–50.
31. Einset, J. and Barbara Imhoff. 1949. Chromosome numbers of apple varieties and sports. II. Proc. Amer. Soc. Hort. Sci. 53:197–201.
32. Einset, J. and Barbara Lamb. 1951. Chromosome numbers of apple varieties and sports. III. Proc. Amer. Soc. Hort. Sci. 58:103–108.
33. Ellenwood, C. W. 1927. Varieties of apples in Ohio. II. Ohio Agr. Exp. Sta. Bull. 411.
34. Ellenwood, C. W., A. L. Harris, and F. S. Howlett. 1942. Fruit varieties for Ohio. Ohio Agr. Exp. Sta. Bull. 627.
35. Gourley, J. H. and C. W. Ellenwood. 1926. Fruit varieties in Ohio. I. Ohio Agr. Exp. Sta. Bull. 391:427–438.
36. Green, W. J., Paul Thayer and J. B. Keil. 1915. Varieties of apples in Ohio. Ohio Agr. Exp. Sta. Bull. 290.
37. Howlett, F. S. 1927. Apple pollination studies in Ohio. Ohio Agr. Exp. Sta. Bull. 404.
38. Howlett, F. S. and C. W. Ellenwood. 1952. New Ruby apple. Ohio Farm and Home Res. 37 (277):51,66.
39. Magness, J. R. 1941. Apple varieties and important producing

sections of the United States. U. S. Dept. Agr. Farm Bull.
1883.

40. Mowry, J. B. 1963. Apple variety performance in southern Illinois. Trans. Ill. State Hort. Soc. 97:134–144.

41. Mowry, J. B. 1964. Maximum orchard susceptibility of pear and
apple varieties to fire blight. Plant Dis. Reptr. 48 (4):-
272–276.

42. Oberle, G. D. 1969. Fruit Var. Hort. Dig. 23:3.

43. Ragan, W. H. 1905. Nomenclature of the apple. U. S. Dept. Agr.
Pl. Ind. Bull. 56.

44. Shaw, J. K. 1943. Descriptions of apple varieties. Mass. Agr. Exp.
Sta. Bull. 403.

45. Taylor, W. A. 1907. Promising new fruits. USDA Yearbook Agr.,
305–320.

46. Waltman, C. S. 1939. Tree fruit varieties for Kentucky. Ky. Agr.
Exp. Sta. Bull. 394:183–231.

# X. WINESAP

E.S. DEGMAN
Horticulturist *(retired)*,

Tree Fruit Research Center,
Wenatchee, Washington

THE WINESAP WAS GROWN BY THE EARLY PIONEERS OF THE
United States. Its origin is not known for sure. In 1817 Coxe (5)
reported that it was then fast becoming "the most favorite cider
fruit in West Jersey." Since his book does not contain a bibliography and there appears to be no earlier references to this
variety, it has been assumed that Winesap originated in New
Jersey probably prior to 1800. However, it should be empha-
sized that this is merely an assumption. Winesap was one of the
leading varieties grown in the United States until about 1950.
Since then the production of this variety has fallen off, and few
new plantings are being made. This decline has been associated
with the development of controlled atmosphere storage. This
method of storage permits holding other varieties for selling
during the late spring season when Winesap had been predomi-
nant.

The characteristics of the Winesap tree and fruits are given
by S.A. Beach, *et al* (1). It is a diploid variety with pink blos-
soms in contrast to the white of most apple varieties. Its flowers
produce little if any viable pollen, therefore, Winesap is not a
good pollinizer for itself or any other variety. It should be
picked in a period 155 to 165 days from full bloom, about 10
days after Delicious in the State of Washington. Winesap stores
so well in cold storage that practically no use is being made of

TABLE 1. Sports of Winesap

| Name | Origin | | | Color |
|------|--------|---|---|-------|
| | Where | When | How | |
| Virginia | Garland Orchards, Troutville, Va. | 1922 | whole tree | darker than parent |
| Mosebar | Howard S. Mosebar, Yakima, Wash. | 1923 | limb | striped |
| Stull | Gilbert orchard, Yakima, Wash. | about 1928 | limb | blushed |
| Strand | C. G. Strand, Cowiche, Wash. | 1928 | whole tree | mostly blushed |
| Swanson No. 1 | Anton Swanson, Peshastin, Wash. | about 1931 | whole tree | blushed |
| Marley | Marley Orchards, Tieton, Wash. | 1935 | whole tree | striped |
| Houser | Lawrence E. Houser, Selah, Wash. | about 1935 | limb | blushed |
| Farrington* | E. T. Farrington, Wenatchee, Wash. | 1939 | limb | striped |
| Allen | Allen Bros., Naches, Wash. | about 1939 | whole trees | striped |
| Baxters Black (3, List 2) | Frederick K. Baxter, Nauvoo, Ill. | about 1940 | | striped |
| Welch No. 1 | Jim Welch, Wenatchee, Wash. | about 1940 | whole trees | blushed |
| Welch No. 2 | Jim Welch, Wenatchee, Wash. | about 1940 | whole trees | mostly striped |
| Gensinger No. 1 | Ed Gensinger, Rock Island, Wash. | about 1940 | whole trees | striped |
| Gensinger No. 2 | Ed Gensinger, Rock Island, Wash. | about 1940 | whole trees | blushed |
| Goodner (3, List 13) | J. C. Goodner, Wenatchee, Wash. | 1942 | limb | striped |
| Improved Seeando | Hemminger Bros., Wenatchee, Wash. | about 1945 | whole trees | striped |
| Neubert | H. Neubert, Tieton, Wash. | about 1945 | limb | striped |
| Johnson (Cooper) | Nick Cooper, Wenatchee, Wash. | 1946 | limb | striped |
| King | A. W. King Wenatchee, Wash. | 1947 | limb | striped |
| Ruble | Alfred E. Ruble Wenatchee, Wash. | about 1949 | whole trees | striped |
| Wade | J. M. Wade Malott, Wash. | 1950 | whole trees | mostly blushed |
| Swanson No. 3 | Anton Swanson, Peshastin, Wash. | 1950 | whole tree | striped |
| Felker | G. L. Felker, Chelan, Wash. | 1951 | limb | blushed |

* Spur type

TABLE 1. Sports of Winesap (continued)

| Name | Origin | | | Color |
|------|--------|--|--|-------|
| | Where | When | How | |
| Jylha | Eino Jylha, Tieton, Wash. | 1951 | limb | blushed |
| Rogan | Leo P. Rogan, Selah, Wash. | about 1952 | limb | blushed |
| Crimson | Ford Hoevis, Zillah, Wash. | 1953 | whole trees | striped |
| Cooper-Madden | Cooper-Madden Orchard | about 1954 | whole tree | striped |
| Birchmont | Birchmont Orchards Wenatchee, Wash. | 1955 | limb (tetraploid) | striped |
| Pasley Grant | Clinton Pasley, Brewster, Wash. | 1955 | limb | striped |
| Mance* | Rudy Mance, Naches, Wash. | about 1956 | whole tree | striped |
| Schell* | Clarence Schell, Cashmere, Wash. | 1957 | limb | blushed |
| Sinclair | Sinclair Orchards, Oliver, B.C. | 1958 | | blushed |

* Spur type

CA storage for it. Sales are largely for fresh fruit but lower grades are sometimes used to make a very acceptable juice.

***Strains of Winesap*** Strains are of two types, either striped or blushed. These terms are rather empirical. They refer to the manner in which color is deposited on the apples. This can be determined when the color is forming on the apple since at that time an apple is definitely a blushed type or a striped type. Later, the stripes merge so that at harvest time often it is impossible to determine whether an apple is a blushed or striped type (Fig. 1). All blushed types which have been found to date are susceptible to a type of russet. The cause of this russet is not known but the amount of it varies from year to year.

The *Virginia Winesap* originated as a whole tree sport in the Garland orchards near Troutville, Virginia. It was selected by Paul Stark, Sr. about 1922 and was propagated extensively until the late 1940's. The terms "Virginia Winesap" and "Old Fashion Winesap" have also been used to distinguish between this variety and the Stayman Winesap. Many growers of Winesap noticed that there was considerable variation in the color of the fruit on different trees in their orchards. For a while they merely propagated from the higher colored ones but later these strains were selected and named.

One strain called *Black Winesap* originated in the Remley orchard at Dryden, Wash. in 1927 (3, List 14). This strain was propagated for several years but is no longer in use because of its susceptibility to russet skin. Some felt also that it produced small apples. Blodgett and Aichele (2) have described 32 of these strains essentially as shown in Table 1.

Other sports of lesser importance are Kelner, Newell, Griffith, Gardiner, Carl, D2324 (Double Red), Pichas, Swanson #2.

As mentioned by Blodgett and Aichele (2), about 1923 on the farm of Howard Mosebar, a Winesap tree sported to form the *Mosebar Red Winesap* (3, List 12). Although there may be slight variation in the appearance of some strains and these may have been given names, many strains have their origin in the Mosebar strain.

One of the sports mentioned by Blodgett and Aichele is the *Birchmont Winesap*. It was discovered in 1955. It was obviously a polyploid. Later studies, as reported by Magness and Dermen (7), indicated that it was an internally tetraploid sport and since the sexual tissue was tetraploid, it could be used in a breeding program to get triploid seedlings of Winesap. This variety has been used in breeding work to a limited extent, but, to date, no fruiting seedlings have been reported.

Another tetraploid Winesap sport has been developed by Dermen (6). Starting with a 2–2–4 Winesap, an adventitious bud developed into a shoot which was determined to be tetraploid in all layers and is known as the *4–4–4 Winesap*. Like the Birchmount Winesap, the 4–4–4 Winesap is useful in breeding work only. *Doud Giant Winesap #20* originated as a bud sport in the L.J. Doud orchards at Roann, Ind. It had unusually large

size and was sent to Geneva, N.Y. in 1959 where it was determined to be a diploid-tetraploid chimera.

The *Double Red Winesap* (3, List 17) originated as a bud
sport in 1948 at Aspers, Penn. It is reported to have more red
color than Winesap.

Some of the strains listed by Blodgett and Aichele (2) are spur
type trees. They are smaller, heavier producing trees having
more spurs but fewer lateral limbs. The leader limbs are more
upright and rigid so that the trees, in addition to being smaller,
are also less spreading than a standard tree. Other spur types are
the whole tree sports of *Oscar Thornton*, Oroville, Wash. and
*Del Law*, Orondo, Wash. Probably what happened in these
instances is that the nurseries propagating regular Winesaps had
spur type sports occur in their scion blocks. They were not
aware of this and propagated trees from these sports. As a
result, several whole tree sports might appear in one orchard.
This could happen easily also with sports not spur type. Sometimes a spur type sport occurs and is allowed to grow on the tree
where it originated. This is what happened in the *A. W. King*
orchard in Wenatchee, Wash. This is a limb sport and has not
been propagated further. It is unfortunate that to date no spur
type Winesap has been reported which also has more color than
standard Winesap.

## DESCENDENTS OF WINESAP

Among the seedlings of Winesap is the Stayman Winesap.
According to Beach (1), "The Stayman Winesap resulted from
a seedling of Winesap grown by Mr. J. Stayman of Leaven-
worth, Kan. in 1866." It has been planted extensively in the
Shenandoah Valley where it grows to perfection. Stayman
Winesap fruits crack rather severely in some seasons. This variety also has many sports. A block of Stayman Winesap was
planted near Lake Chelan, Wash. in 1906. When these trees
were bearing, a branch was observed to bear darker fruit than
the rest. This strain was called the *Blaxstayman* and was spread

throughout the country. Later the Blaxstayman sported again near Wenatchee, Wash. and this sport is known as *Improved Blaxstayman No. 201* (3, List 5). The *Neipling*, as reported in List No. 14 of Brooks and Olmo (3), is said to be also a sport of Blaxstayman and although it originated in New Jersey, it is similar to Improved Blaxstayman No. 201.

The *Cardinal Stayman* is reported in List No. 18 of Brooks and Olmo (3) to have originated as a bud mutation of Stayman Winesap at Mount Jackson, Va. in 1945. It is said to have a bright red skin.

The *Staymared* originated in Covington, Va. in 1926 (3, List 3). It is a bud mutation of Stayman Winesap.

Another seedling of Winesap is the *Golden Winesap*. As described by Campbell (4), it is a seedling of Winesap grown by C.E. Bennett, Ogden, Utah. This apple does not resemble Winesap, but is a large yellow apple with a definite blush on the cheek. The fruit of Golden Winesap is reported to be of good quality, but the tree is very susceptible to mildew.

The *Turley* apple is thought by many to be a seedling of Winesap but some think it may be a seedling of Stayman. The original tree was discovered in Joe Burton's orchard, Lawrence County, Ind. in 1900 (3, List 6). Turley is a large apple similar to Stayman, but it does not crack. However, it has lower eating quality than Stayman and does not have the storage quality of Winesap. It was planted extensively in the 1930's but is losing in popularity now (1969).

*Shenandoah.* Winesap x Opalescent, is a 1968 introduction of the Virginia Polytechnic Institute, Blacksburg. It matures just before Delicious and is recommended for early midseason processing. It has an attractive blush color, firm flesh, tart flavor, and keeps well in storage.

## Literature Cited

1. Beach, S.A., N.O. Booth and O.M. Taylor, 1905. The apples of New York, N.Y. Agr. Exp. Sta. Rep. 1903. Vol. I.

2. Blodgett, E.C. and Murit Aichele. 1960. Washington State Department of Agriculture Hort. Bulletin #3.
3. Brooks R.M. and H.P. Olmo. Register of new fruit and nut varieties —Lists 2, 3, 5, 6, 12, 13, 14, 17 and 18. Proc. Amer. Soc. Hort. Sci. 47:544–569; 50:426–442; 56:509–537; 58:386–407; 70:557–584; 72:519–541; 74:758–785; 81:568–600; and 83:862–882.
4. Campbell, W.G. 1916. The Fruit Grower. St. Joseph, Missouri.
5. Coxe, Wm. 1817. Fruit trees.
6. Dermen, Haig. 1955. A homogeneous tetraploid shoot from 2–2–4 type chimeral Winesap apple. J. Heredity. 43:8.
7. Magness, J.R. and Haig Dermen. 1957. An internal polyploid sport of Winesap apple. Proc. Amer. Soc. Hort. Sci. 69:65–67.

Valuable information has also been received from the following:
W.D. Armstrong. L.P. Batjer, Haig Dermen, D.V. Fisher, Edwin Gould, Aubrey D. Hibbard, W.J. Kender, G.D. Oberle, R. Shay, Jr., J.J. Snyder, R.E. Snyder, Paul Stark, Jr., Clarence Swanson, R.B. Tukey, Peter VanWell, Sr., Roger D. Way.

FIG. 1. A red strain of Winesap, striped type.

# XI. YORK IMPERIAL

H.A. ROLLINS, Jr., head

Department of Horticulture, Virginia Polytechnic Institute
Blacksburg, Virginia

THE YORK IMPERIAL HAS, FOR MANY YEARS, DOMINATED THE apple industry of the concentrated Appalachian fruit producing area extending from northern Virginia to southern Pennsylvania. It is still the leading variety of this area, but 1969 planting trends indicate that it may soon give way to red Delicious. While York Imperial is primarily a processing variety, some of the improved red strains are packed and sold on the fresh market in late winter and early spring.

## HISTORY

York Imperial dates back to the early 1800's when it was found on the farm of a Mr. Johnson adjoining what then was the borough of York, Pa. Johnson was attracted to the tree by school boys visiting it in the early spring to pick up apples that had passed the winter on the ground covered by leaves. On checking, he found that the fruit was in good condition. The next fall, when the crop was ripe, he took samples to a local nurseryman, Jonathan Jessop, who began propagating the variety prior to 1830 under the name of Johnson's Fine Winter. The apple was known by this name until the middle of the century when Charles Downing examined specimens of it and pronounced it the "Imperial of Keepers", and suggested that it be named York Imperial. Mr. Jessop found little demand for the trees at first and dumped the surplus from his nursery into a hollow beside the turnpike passing his place. These trees were picked up by farmers returning from market and taken home for planting on their own farms in the lower end of York County, Pa. After the commercial merit of the variety was recognized, trees became widely distributed throughout Pennsylvania, Maryland, West Virginia, and Virginia; and it became the leading variety of the area. As far as is known, this variety was first described in print by Dr. W.D. Brinckle in 1853 (1).

During the early 1900's, York Imperial gained in popularity throughout the Appalachian region due to an active export business with England. Because of its keeping qualities and because it possessed fruit characteristics that appealed to the English people, this business was quite profitable and flourished until about 1930 when British import restrictions sharply changed the markets for apples throughout the Appalachian area. With the loss of the export market, emphasis was then placed on developing new domestic outlets. It was difficult to sell York Imperial apples in competition with the red varieties, and only the better grades were in demand. Fortunately, at this time, the processing industry expanded through utilization of the lower grades of York Imperial and other varieties. However, it was largely a salvage-type operation.

During World War II, the demand for processed apple products increased and it became apparent that there was a real potential for York Imperial in processed apple products. Fruit processors further expanded their operations and intensified their efforts to develop new markets, the result being that apple processing in the Appalachian area became more than a salvage operation and the growers began producing fruit for this specific market.

## GENERAL CHARACTERISTICS

York Imperial is probably best characterized by its lopsided

(1) Much of the early history was taken from the discussion of York Imperial in Volume I of *"Apples of New York"* by S.A. Beach.

appearance. It is an apple that is flattened, poorly colored, and firm to hard at harvest. The flesh of the fruit is a creamy yellow giving an attractive color to processed products made from it (Fig. 1).

FIG. 1.   Typical York Imperial Apples

York Imperial did not gain its initial popularity strictly as a cooking apple, but it does possess many desirable canning characteristics and, consequently, apple processors normally pay a premium for it. One important consideration is the high yield of processed product that can be produced from a given weight of raw fruit. This is in part due to the flatness of the apple and the small core in relation to the total volume of the apple. York slices hold their shape in the can and York sauce has a yellow appearance that is preferred in a number of markets.

York Imperial is considered a winter apple, maturing after Stayman but before Winesap. Growers, however, frequently extend the harvest of this variety over as much as a six-week period since specific harvest date is not a critical factor for fruit that is to be processed. York Imperial is a very firm apple at harvest, resists bruising, and stores well. These characteristics were responsible for its early popularity as an export variety. These same characteristics have made it a preferred processing variety since it will remain in acceptable condition longer than other varieties when piled loose in the processing lot. The current trend (1969) is for larger volumes of fruit to be placed in both conventional refrigerated and controlled atmosphere storage to extend the processing period to more nearly a year round operation.

York Imperial is moderately tolerant of the more common apple diseases in the Appalachian area, apple scab and powdery mildew. It is quite susceptible to cedar rusts and fire blight. Fire blight is such a serious problem that, on vigorously growing young trees, the use of antibiotic sprays during the bloom period is a common precautionary practice against the destruction of scaffold limbs by the disease. Normally, larger bearing trees are not treated.

One of the more serious problems related to the commercial production of this variety is its susceptibility to the physiological disorder, York spot, or cork spot. This is characterized by 1/4, or even larger, corky areas in the flesh of the fruit. When these corky spots are near the surface, they result in sunken or depressed areas clearly visible prior to harvest. Cork spot should not be confused with boron deficiency which causes a slight browning in the core area. York is less susceptible to visible boron deficiency symptoms than many other varieties. Some reduction in cork spot of York has been obtained through the use of soluble boron sprays during the bloom and early postbloom period. While these sprays have occasionally reduced the severity of the disorder in serious corking situations, they have in no way provided a solution. Seriously corked fruit is of little value for the fresh market and, for processing, results in excessive trimming, which greatly increases labor cost and reduces yield.

In orchards where fruit is produced solely for the processor, large size and high yields per acre are important. Red color development and smooth finish are of little importance. Consequently, the variety is usually grown under higher than normal rates of nitrogen fertilization and less than normal detailed pruning. Due to its tolerance to apple scab and powdery mildew, York can be satisfactorily produced with an abbreviated spray program.

Within recent years the development of red strains has resulted in a limited volume of York Imperial apples being packed and sold for fresh consumption. There is a good demand for this variety in some markets late in the storage season. York is quite susceptible to apple scald but recently developed scald control techniques have reduced its incidence.

The York Imperial tree is typically large with an upright habit of growth. It is a relatively easy tree to grow and to maintain. It is a common practice to make only a few large pruning cuts each year and to do very little detailed pruning. Where fruit is being produced for the canner, this practice is quite satisfactory. While very productive, York trees do possess a strong tendency toward alternate bearing if such a cycle once becomes established. Within recent years, however, the widespread use of chemical thinning sprays has minimized the problem. York Imperial responds well to the use of both naphthalene acetic acid and naphthylacetamide.

As the availability of harvest labor becomes more restricted each year, more consideration to the potential of an individual variety for mechanical harvesting becomes essential. This is particularly important for processing fruit. York fruits can be harvested with shake and catch systems with a minimum reduction in the value of the fruit to the processor. The upright habit of main scaffold limbs facilitates under the tree movement of equipment. The tendency for the fruit to set heavily around the periphery of the tree minimizes the damage to fruit falling through the tree. Because of the short stem, fruit removal by shaking is relatively complete. Also of significance is the fact that the firmness of York fruits prevents excessive bruising. Growers and processors alike would prefer to continue to harvest the crop by hand but other practical solutions are available should they become necessary.

The trend is toward smaller trees, and in some of the more recent plantings, York Imperial trees are being set out at close spacing on one of the size controlling rootstocks. While information as to the response of this variety to the various clonal stocks is limited, preliminary indications are that MM 106 gives a good semidwarf tree. York on EM VII has not been as satisfactory.

## STRAINS

*Colora Red York (Red York Imperial).* Originated in Colora, Cecil County, Md. by Lloyd Balderson, III. Introduced commercially in the fall of 1935. Patent No. 168, March 10, 1936. Bud mutation of York Imperial discovered October 10, 1933. *Fruit:* Colors a full bright red without any stripe, uniformly in all parts of the tree; other characteristics identical with York Imperial. *Tree:* identical with York Imperial.

*York-A-Red.* Originated in Hedgesville, W. Va. by Paul L. Lingamfelter. Introduced commercially in 1937. Patent No. 258, July 20, 1937. Bud mutation of York Imperial discovered in 1931. *Fruit:* identical with York Imperial except for all-over red color.

*Yorking (Red York Imperial, Red Yorking).* Originated in Shippensburg, Pa. by the Allison Estate. Introduced commercially in 1932. Patent No. 125, May 28, 1935. Bud mutation of York Imperial discovered about 1925. *Fruit:* color all red instead of partly red as on parent tree.

*West Virginia Red York.* Originated in Roanoke, W. Va. by John
L. Hevener, Roanoke Nursery. Introduced in 1962. Plant patent 2,288, October 8, 1963. Bud mutation of York Imperial
discovered in 1950. *Fruit:* large, up to 3 inches in diameter,
conical, slightly angular; skin solid red, thick, tough, smooth,
waxed, dots many and small; flesh white, rather juicy, firm,
crisp, flavor mild, very good quality, small core; keeps very well;
ripens in mid October, about 1 or 2 weeks after York Imperial;
resembles Yorking. *Tree:* size medium, very productive, bears
regularly, hardy.

## FUTURE

All indications are that the York Imperial will remain an
important variety in the Appalachian area for many years particularly if cork spot can be solved. The demand for processed
apple products continues to expand and there is no other variety
produced in the area that combines so many desirable processing qualities.

# ERRATA

*Unfortunately, during the printing of Chapter 12, the captions to the illustrations were omitted. They are as follows:*

FIG. 1. (Pg. 156) Relative inherent leaf area of several apple rootstock clones and the reduced leaf area obtained with inadequate water supply.

FIG. 2. (Pg. 156) Nongrafted rootstock clones as grown in the greenhouse. The 2 left plants are MM 111 and the 2 plants to the right are MM 106. The tall plant in each case received optimum water during 8 weeks showing the importance of adequate soil moisture.

FIG. 3. (Pg. 159) Fruiting of Red Delicious/EM IX in second year in orchard. It is recommended to remove most of the fruit to allow more tree growth at this age.

FIG. 4. (Pg. 168) Left: Hardwood cutting of MM 106 rooted during the winter and budded (14″ high) with the variety the following season. Right: Three cuttings of EM VII similarly rooted and budded.

FIG. 5. (Pg. 170) Flower production per linear foot of shoot growth as induced by different interstems on Golden Delicious top. Seedling rootstock. The most dwarfing interstem was EM VIII, the least dwarfing, Robin.

FIG. 6. (Pg. 172) A three year old hedgerow planting of Golden Delicious, with EM VII interstem and Columbia seedling root system, planted 6 × 15 feet.

FIG. 7. (Pg. 173) Stem pitting virus showing in the Virginia Crab rootstock and no similar symptoms apparent on the Golden Delicious top. Note also suckering tendencies of this rootstock.

FIG. 8. (Pg. 175) Top—Diagramatic illustrations of the hedgerom system of planting with a tree spacing of 12 × 24 feet. Bottom—The off-set system using either EM IX or EM 26 as rootstock for the off-set trees. The permanent trees (12 × 24 feet) could be on either MM 106, MM 111 or EM VII rootstocks.

# XII. ROOTSTOCKS IN RELATION TO APPLE CULTIVARS

R.F. CARLSON
Department of Horticulture,

Michigan State University,
East Lansing, Michigan

THE ROOT SYSTEM OF THE TREE IS VERY IMPORTANT IN THE production of quality apple trees and fruit. In fact, it is as important as the variety which it supports. The main reasons for this are: 1) it anchors the tree, 2) it supplies the variety with mineral nutrients and water, 3) it determines tree size and form, 4) it controls flowering and fruiting, 5) it improves fruit size and color, 6) it imparts hardiness or tenderness to the scion, and 7) it, in part, influences branch form and leaf fall.

Dwarfing rootstocks have come to the fore in recent years in North America mainly because of the need to control tree size. In Europe, rootstocks have been of concern for centuries due to lack of space for large trees. French Crab apple seedlings were used extensively both in America and Europe in the early part of this century. Red Delicious seedlings were used as the main rootstock source in this country prior to 1955. Various seedling selections of *Malus* sp. were vegetatively propagated in Europe under different names prior to their classification at East Malling Research Station, England in 1912. Before describing some of the presently used dwarfing rootstocks, it is important that the reader learns the qualities in them.

## QUALITIES IN ROOTSTOCKS

*Anchorage.* The use of free standing trees has been, and still is, the general orchard practice in this country in contrast to various training forms used in Europe. However, since 1950 the demand here for smaller free standing trees has increased. For this reason, one of the qualities in a rootstock is a strong, well developed root system permitting trees to grow without support, both in windy and protected sites. The roots need to be strong, composed of fibrous root tissues, to prevent snapping off under unusual stress. Rootstocks having brittle roots, such as EM IX[1] and EM VIII, are often in need of support in the form of stakes or trellises.

The roots should be present on all sides of the stock, rather than on one side. Stocks with a one sided root system, such as EM IV and MM 109, tend to produce trees which lean due to poor anchorage. Uniformly spreading roots are preferred to the tap root type of root system. The shallow spreading root system (EM XIII, MM 111 and MM 106) are preferred in some locations where a high water table prevails at certain times of the year, or where a hardpan soil prevents deep root penetration. The rootstocks with spreading root systems which naturally tend to penetrate deeper (EM VII and MM 104)[1] are ideal on the well drained deep types of soil.

*Efficiency in Water and Nutrient Uptake.* Although the rootstock clones differ in their root growth characteristics, their efficiency in nutrient and water uptake is not as striking. The entire gamut of rootstocks has not been studied and compared in detail as to uptake and translocation efficiencies. In a nutritional study of six rootstocks, it was found that varieties on EM V and EM II were not as efficient in K-uptake; and EM I in Mg-uptake, as compared to trees on EM XVI (2). EM VII nongrafted plants exhibited various growth responses when grown on soils with different mineral or nutrient deficiencies. Without iron, plants

---

[1]EM and MM are the abbreviations of East Malling and Malling Merton respectively.

were stunted; with minus magnesium, defoliation resulted; and with minus iron and magnesium, both stunting and early defoliation occurred (10). In another study of mineral composition of apple leaves, it was found that trees on EM IX had higher calcium and magnesium content than those on EM VII, and trees on EM II had higher phosphorus, calcium and magnesium content than those on EM XVI (16). Thus, there is an obvious difference of leaf mineral composition as influenced by the root system.

TABLE 1. Water consumed and comparative growth
of rootstock clones

| Clones | Avg. water consumed (ml) | | | Difference in water consumption relative to Delicious seedling (%) | Growth range[1] |
|---|---|---|---|---|---|
| | Low | High | Difference | | |
| R. Del. seedlings | 2164 | 4227 | 2063 | Control | 6 |
| EM II | 2478 | 5298 | 2820 | +27 | 3 |
| Robusta 5 | 2277 | 4947 | 2670 | +24 | 11 |
| Alnarp 2 | 2643 | 5122 | 2479 | +18 | 4 |
| MM 106 | 2710 | 4937 | 2227 | +7 | 9 |
| EM VII | 2770 | 4936 | 2166 | +5 | 12 |
| EM 26 | 2886 | 4975 | 2089 | — | 10 |
| MM 109 | 2633 | 4683 | 2050 | — | 5 |
| MM 104 | 2373 | 3967 | 1694 | −18 | 7 |
| MM 111 | 2811 | 4418 | 1607 | −22 | 8 |
| EM IX | 2934 | 4434 | 1500 | −27 | 1 |
| EM XII | 2580 | 3307 | 827 | −59 | 2 |

[1] 12 = Greatest terminal growth; 1 = Least growth

Similarly, there is a difference in efficiency of water use among rootstocks. In a recent study under controlled condi-

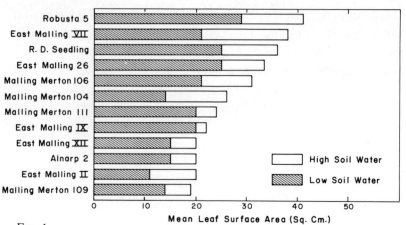

FIG. 1.

FIG. 2.

tions, MM 104 and MM 111 (nongrafted) respectively consumed 18 and 22% less water than Red Delicious seedlings,
based on difference between low and high water level and yet,
produced more terminal growth (Table 1). Low water level gave
the least terminal growth (Fig. 1). The most "efficient" rootstocks based on water use and growth were: MM 111, MM 104,
MM 109, MM 106, and EM VII; and the "least efficient" were:
Robusta 5, Alnarp 2, EM II and EM IX (4). The efficient use
of water by any plant is extremely important on sandy sites
where rain is infrequent. In other words, a plant efficient in
water use can be said to show a degree of drought tolerance.
Varieties on MM 111 have shown such drought tolerance in
orchard tests. This may also be associated with the inherent leaf
area of the particular clone, each having a certain leaf size (Fig.
2).

*Size Control.* Another very important quality of the rootstock is
that it must be able to impart a certain degree of dwarfing on
the scion variety grafted on it. Once the degree of dwarfing to
a particular rootstock clone has been established, it falls into a
certain orchard use category and, often, a use category as far as
a particular variety is concerned. That is, certain scion varieties
perform more harmoniously on certain rootstocks with specific
dwarfing effects, according to the vigor of each plant, the scion
and the stock. For example: Jonathan on EM II and Red Delicious on MM 106 are examples of compatible dwarfing combinations.

   A partial explanation for this difference in behabior of scion
varieties on certain clones lies in the relationship of the two and
in the inherent vigor of each. That is, certain strains, varieties,
or species (in both rootstocks and scions) manifest their difference when combined in graft union. Each exerts an influence on
the other partner. The seat of most of this effect is at the contact
area in the graft union where the two may unite in perfect order,
or to a lesser degree when one part will overgrow the other.
However, overgrowth or undergrowth of one or the other part

of the graft component may not necessarily indicate incompatibility. Rather, the efficiency (physiological) of each component to get along in growth with the other constitutes congeniality. The differences accounting for this agreement in growth of the two are many for example, biochemical influence, cell size of the anatomical parts, and the arrangement of the wood tissues at the immediate graft union. All these and other detailed factors are involved in controlling the size of the tree.

Each rootstock clone has its own degree of dwarfing which shows up in the scion variety in the form of smaller tree stature and earlier bearing (Fig. 3 and Table 2).

*Flower and Fruit Control.* Some of the factors involved in vegetative growth control also influence flowering and fruiting. For example, it is not precisely known why EM IX will bring a tardy variety into fruiting sooner than EM VII. The carbohydrate/nitrogen relationship is part of the explanation. That certain auxins or hormone-like substances are active in causing or preventing flowering is becoming more evident. In 1967 it was found that growth-controlling factors were present in EM II and MM 106. The factor which stimulates root formation in Mung bean cuttings was present in both clones. The EM II clone also contained a root inhibiting substance. These growth controlling substances were found by chromatographic separations of extracts from these two clones (1). Since these substances were found in the stems of the clones, it is possible that flower stimulating or flower inhibiting materials could also be located in the wood part or in the buds of rootstock clones. Very detailed research could solve some of the mysteries. At present it is a known fact that each dwarfing clone has a certain flower stimulatory influence on the scion variety. Similarly, each scion variety has a built in flowering stimulus causing it to bear early or late in its life cycle. Extreme examples are Golden Delicious, a very precocious variety and Northern Spy, a very tardy fruiting variety. Red Delicious/EM IX will fruit at the tender age of two years. (Fig. 3).

FIG. 3.

TABLE 2.   Examples of apple variety/rootstock combinations and
comparative size (at 8 years) in per cent of the same
variety on seedling rootstock

| | Rootstock | | | | | | | |
|---|---|---|---|---|---|---|---|---|
| Variety | EM IX | EM 26 | EM VII | MM 106 | EM II | MM 111 | Alnarp 2 | Seedling |
| Delicious | | | | | | | | |
| Regular | 35 | 40 | 45 | 55 | 65 | 70 | 75 | 100 |
| Spur | 25 | 30 | 35 | 40 | 50 | 55 | 65 | 90 |
| G. Delicious | 30 | 35 | 45 | 50 | 60 | 70 | 70 | 70 |
| McIntosh | 35 | 40 | 50 | 55 | 60 | 65 | 70 | 100 |
| Jonathan | 25 | 30 | 40 | 45 | 60 | 65 | 70 | 100 |
| R.I. Greening | 30 | 35 | 45 | 50 | 60 | 70 | 70 | 100 |
| N. Spy | 35 | 40 | 45 | 50 | 60 | 65 | 75 | 100 |

*Fruit Size and Color.* The fruit size, especially on young dwarfed trees, is larger than on standard trees. The bearing surface is distributed uniformly throughout the tree, contributing to better fruit spacing and this in turn often results in larger fruit. In smaller trees more light reaches the foliage increasing its efficiency in food synthesis (11). However, in mature dwarf orchards, fruit size is directly related to fruit thinning with most varieties.

Fruit color is generally better on compact trees due to less shading from overhanging branches. Many dwarfed fruit trees begin to bear fruit in the first four years, causing the young flexible branches to bend outward, exposing more foliage and fruit to light and thus improving fruit color over that of standard trees.

*Hardiness Control.* All plants are endowed with a built in mechanism which protects and supports them under stress of low or high temperatures. For example: the cactus plant has water storing tissues and tough epidermis to protect it against drought and high temperatures. Temperate plants are able to move some water from one part to another in the fall to withstand freezing temperatures in the winter. These control mechanisms vary in the different apple varieties and apple clones. That is, some can apparently tolerate lower winter temperatures than others. The ability of the plant to harden-off in the fall is very important. The time of defoliation of these clones in the fall plays an important role in their capacity to go through the winter without injury. Early defoliation in a variety or clone is an indication that the plant is hardening off and getting ready for lower temperatures.

Some examples of early defoliation in the fall are EM VII and MM 111 and those late in defoliation, MM 106 and EM 26. Jonathan and Golden Delicious are early and Northern Spy and Grimes Golden are late in defoliation.

Other factors contributing to hardiness are such conditions as short or long dormancy periods inherent in the rootstock and variety. If the clone or the variety loses its dormancy on warm days in January, then it is more subject to winter injury. The thick bark of EM IX tends to be less tolerant to low temperature than the thin bark of EM VII which tends to harden off sooner. These are but a few examples of the adaptibility and hardiness of different clones to varying climatic conditions.

## ROOTSTOCK DESCRIPTIONS.

For the sake of simplicity, brevity, and to avoid repetition of other published information, only the presently commercially used and available rootstocks will be considered in this chapter. For further descriptive details of these and many other dwarfing rootstocks, the reader is referred to Chapter 7, *Dwarfed Fruit Trees* (14).

The clonal rootstocks used for dwarfing apple trees in America originated in different locations in Europe. They were collected, described and classified at the East Malling Research Station 1912–1917. This was, and still is, the East Malling (EM) clone rootstock series with Roman numerals.

The Malling Merton (MM) clonal rootstock series originated in England in the early 1920's by breeding rootstocks with a purpose in mind—namely, resistance to woolly aphid, improved anchorage, scion compatibility, precocity and other characteristics. This project was initiated jointly by the East Malling Research Station and the John Innes Horticultural Institute at Merton and hence, the name Malling Merton. The MM series are hybrids of Northern Spy and certain EM clones and were given the numbers MM 101 to MM 115. Two of these are now in use in United States, namely MM 106 and MM 111. MM 109 was discontinued due to tree leaning tendencies and MM 104, unsatisfactory growth in poorly drained soils.

The rootstocks described here will be in order of relative dwarfing effect from small to large.

*EM VIII.* Commercial apple varieties budded on EM VIII will produce small bush type trees slightly smaller than those on EM

IX. The wood is brittle, but not as brittle as EM IX, and for this reason it is suggested for use as an intermediate stem section (see section on Interstem Method of Dwarfing). When used either as the root system or as the intermediate stem section, the trees need special training to obtain a height of 6–8 feet. Individual or trellis support is essential when EM VIII is the root system, but when used as an intermediate stemsection, no support is needed if a vigorous rootstock is used. EM VIII is not readily available. It is similar to the Clark Dwarf rootstock in plant characteristics.

*EM IX.* For truly small trees this rootstock is excellent. However, it has certain peculiarities which must be understood in order to obtain maximum tree performance. The wood and roots are brittle and, therefore, the trees must be stake, or trellis, supported. Contrary to some opinions, the root system is not shallow and will be well distributed and deep rooted in a suitable soil. The best soil site of a uniform loam should be selected for trees on EM IX. Irrigation to provide uniform moisture during the growing season will give better tree character and higher yields. Some suckering occurs with this rootstock; however, this is reduced when the trees are budded high and planted deeply in the orchard. In a planting system with close spacing and high tree density per acre, EM IX is ideal. A very careful pruning program designed to maintain a central leader is essential to obtain maximum bearing surface. Most varieties on EM IX will fruit the first and second year, but this is not recommended. Varieties on this rootstock are ideal for the "pick-your-own" apple marketing system.

*EM 26.* This rootstock is similar to EM IX in growth and behavior, but is slightly more vigorous. For this reason, it may be used more extensively in commercial orchards in the future. Only limited tests have been conducted with EM 26 and, therefore, little is known of its hardiness and adaptation to various soil types. It also has brittle roots. The rootstock trunk overgrows the scion which is also a characteristic of EM IX. The bark of both EM IX and EM 26 is thicker than the bark of other rootstocks. Varieties/EM 26 should be used sparingly, perhaps as fillers, in areas where low winter temperature causes trunk damage. The graft union should be kept close to the soil line, but not close enough to allow scion rooting.

*EM VII.* For commercial orchards EM VII has proven to be very productive in this country. In addition, it propagates well and produces uniform trees. Its main disadvantage is suckering; however, trees budded 16 inches high on the stock and planted deeper in the permanent place do not sucker as much and are well anchored. A few trees may require staking, but do not stake until there is a need. Since varieties on EM VII are dwarfed about 50%, the trees can be spaced closely together, 150 or more trees per acre. McIntosh, Spartan and Red Rome are well suited to EM VII. Red Delicious spur type strains also make small compact trees on this rootstock. EM VII is adapted to a wide range of soil types and responds well to fertilizer as prescribed by foliar analysis determinations.

*MM 106.* The MM 106 rootstock propagates easily by hard or softwood cuttings and is also very productive in the stool bed. Varieties budded on MM 106 will produce trees somewhat larger than those on EM VII and for this reason it will not replace EM VII in United States for some time. Both have a place and purpose. The outstanding advantages of varieties on MM 106 are: a) early bearing, b) well anchored, c) nonsuckering and d) productive. One disadvantage is that it appears to be less resistant to collar rot, *Phytophthora cactorum* (Leb. and Cohn) Schröt, than EM VII in some locations. This has not been a problem in Michigan. Red Delicious strains and Northern Spy will come into bearing early on this rootstock. It also induces improved fruit color of McIntosh.

*EM IV.* This rootstock clone has many of the qualities and characteristics of EM VII. It is productive in propagation beds producing many well rooted plants per mother plant. The roots of EM IV tend to form on one side, and therefore trees on it often lean and require support. However, the use of high budding in the nursery and deep planting in the orchard should improve the anchorage. EM IV is not readily available and therefore, its use is limited.

*EM II.* This rootstock is still in use because of certain favorable characteristics. When compared to seedling stock, EM II dwarfs trees about 20 to 30% (15). Varieties especially adapted to EM II are: Jonathan, Cortland, and Northern Spy. EM II does not propagate as well as EM VII or the MM rootstocks. It should not be used where the soil tends to be droughty, but rather on a moisture retaining loam soil; nor should it be used on a heavy clay loam soil because of its leaning characteristics.

*MM 111.* In moisture studies of several rootstocks at East Lansing, Mich., the MM 111 indicated a certain degree of drought tolerance over other rootstocks. It compares to EM II in dwarfing influence upon scion varieties, but it is not as precocious. In general, the tree form produced by MM 111 is not as desirable as others in that it tends to produce more upright trees of the vigorous varieties. MM 111 can be classified as a general purpose root-stock for all varieties with the added advantage of its suitability to the droughtier soils.

*MM 104.* This rootstock is more vigorous than MM 111, but seems to have a definite influence on branch development of the scion variety. With Red Delicious, MM 104 produces a more spreading tree than MM 111. This is most obvious the first six years in the orchard. It does not tolerate wet soils and therefore, should not be used on heavy soils with tight subsoil or on sites where surface water remains for a week or two longer in the spring. For this reason, MM 104 is no longer recommended.

*Alnarp 2.* Some apple producing areas are located where low winter temperatures cause severe damage to tree trunks and branches. In fact, without ample ground cover (mulch, weeds or snow), some rootstocks may not stand these winters. Although Sweden is not a large apple producing country, their research workers have proven that Alnarp 2 is the most dependable rootstock. It is now used over 90% in that country. In dwarfing, Alnarp 2 compares to MM 111 and EM II. It produces a well anchored tree with good tree form. Although, all varieties have not been tested on this rootstock, it can be classed safely as an all purpose stock.

*Robusta No. 5.* This is an introduction from Canada. Similar to Alnarp 2, Robusta No. 5 is a very winter hardy rootstock. Unless grown vigorously in the stool bed, it tends to be thorny and thus difficult to bud. It should not be considered a dwarfing rootstock; however, in areas of a shorter growing season and on the lighter soil types, trees on this stock can be controlled in size. Due to its trunk hardiness, varieties can be budded up to 2 feet high thus minimizing the chance of trunk injury during the winter. Other cold resistant rootstocks are being developed at the Ottawa Research Station, Ontario, Canada.

*Kansas-41.* This is one of several rootstock selections made at Kansas State University. It has a high degree of compatibility with most varieties. The union is smooth even though the stock tends to overgrow the variety trunk. K-41 is vigorous with slight tendency to dwarfing. It merits further trials for certain locations.

*Seedlings.* Apple seedlings, mainly of Red Delicious, have been used for many years. There is an apparent difference in seed source of apple seedlings as to growth behavior, hardiness, and tree uniformity. At East Lansing, Mich. Delcon seedlings have shown to be good in tree uniformity and also in seed germination. Red Delicious and McIntosh seedlings are now used by most nurseries. On the other hand, seeds from the Wealthy variety produce poor seedlings. Apple seedlings have a place as rootstocks for standard trees and in areas where tree growth can be contained within a particular spacing system. They may be used also where larger trees are required for mechanical harvesting equipment.

## PROPAGATION OF ROOTSTOCKS

Dwarfing apple rootstocks are produced by vegetative reproduction in contrast to the seedling rootstocks which are reproduced from seed. In reproduction by vegetative means, all plants are identical. Plants from seed are not exactly like either parent. The dwarfing rootstocks propagated vegetatively are known as clones or clonal rootstocks.

The methods of vegetative propagation are many, but the most common are: stooling, layering, and hardwood and softwood cuttings.

*Stooling.* To initiate a stoolbed, the plants are lined out 18 inches apart in rows 10 feet apart. Then they are allowed to grow one year and the second spring they are cut one inch below the soil surface. From below this cut several shoots will grow that season and these are mounded with soil (or sawdust and peatmoss) during June and July. The soil mixture is worked in around the shoots to a height of 12 inches.

The following fall or spring the mound is removed and the rooted shoots clipped close to the original cut made the previous year. In Oregon this can be done in the fall; however, in Michigan it is safer to remove the newly rooted shoots in the spring to avoid winter injury to the crown of the mother plant. This procedure is repeated each year and each year more rooted shoots are obtained from each mother plant (8). These new cuttings are lined out in the spring in the nursery 4 inches apart in rows 3 feet apart and budded to varieties in August.

Each dwarfing clone differs in its capacity to produce roots. For example, EM VII, MM 106, MM 104, and MM 111 root readily and EM II and EM IX do not root easily. Three hundred to 400 rooted shoots per 100 feet of stoolbed row can be produced per year if properly managed.

*Layering.* The main difference in this method from the stooling method is that the young shoots are bent and pinned into a horizontal position and then mounded with 2 inches of soil or soil-sawdust mixture. The mounding is repeated around the young shoots during the growing season. Several rooted shoots can be obtained from each original shoot. These newly rooted shoots are removed and lined out for budding.

*Hardwood Cuttings.* The use of dormant hardwood cuttings provides a rapid method of increasing dwarfing apple clones. The cuttings are taken in November from vigorously growing hedges. The most vigorous shoots root best. Long 24-inch cuttings are preferred since these can be lined out and budded the same year (6).

Propagation frames or beds are set up containing electric heating cables under a 6-inch layer of the rooting medium of 1:1 peatmoss-sawdust mixture. The medium must be kept uniformly moist during the rooting period. The propagation frames should be in a cool place or in a cold storage where air temperature can be maintained at 35 to 40 F and 90% relative humidity. The basal ends of the cuttings are momentarily dipped in a water solution of 3-indole acetic acid (IBA) at 2000 ppm.

The cuttings will root in 6 to 8 weeks at which time the bottom heat is shut off and the cuttings held until lining-out time. Excessive handling of cuttings will injure roots and reduce field stand. When vigorous cuttings are used, they can be budded the same year (Fig. 4).

*Softwood Cuttings.* Special equipment, such as enclosed plastic tent frames with intermittent mist apparatus, are required for successful rooting of softwood cuttings. Such equipment is available or can be made locally. The softwood method can be used to advantage with such clones as EM VII, MM 106, MM 111 and EM 26 which respond well to this treatment.

The cuttings are taken after the first flush of growth in the spring (in Michigan this is the last week in June to the first week in July) when the shoots are still tender. They should be cut

FIG. 4.

early in the morning to prevent drying of the foliage. The lower leaves of the 8-inch cuttings are removed and then the bottom ends of the cuttings are treated with IBA (150 ppm) and placed in the previously prepared rooting medium. A well aerated media of sand-peatmoss or sawdust-peatmoss is best. Good drainage to remove surplus mist water is very important. After planting is completed, the intermittent mist is started. The time frequency of the mist will vary with location of the chamber and the surrounding temperature.

The cuttings are left in the frame for that summer and then lined out for budding the following spring. If good growth is obtained, the cuttings can be transplanted in the late summer or fall of the same season (depending on location) as the cuttings were taken.

## NURSERY PRACTICE WITH ROOTSTOCKS

*Handling the Rootstock.* In propagating and handling several kinds of rootstocks, it is of utmost importance to prevent them from getting mixed. Mixing the rootstocks can accidentally happen by mislabeling rows and bundles or by dropping rooted cuttings among other kinds of cuttings. It should be avoided because, once mixed, it is very difficult and costly to get them separated and true-to-type. Only persons who know rootstocks and their identity can rogue or separate the mixtures.

*Handling the Trees.* The same careful handling of budded varieties on several rootstocks must be observed in order to have true-to-name trees. This means that both the rootstock and the variety should be true-to-name. Both names should be listed on the label. Most progressive nurserymen have both the rootstock beds and the budded trees inspected once or twice annually by men qualified to identify the varieties.

*Grading Rootstocks and Trees.* In order to improve uniformity and quality of rootstocks, they should be graded into bundles according to size. When the rootstocks are dug from the stoolbeds they should be graded into bundles of small, medium and large. At that time they also should be graded according to degree of rooting—no roots, few roots, and well rooted.

Hardwood cuttings are graded according to size prior to putting them into the propagation beds. Finished trees are graded as to trunk diameter ($\frac{3}{8}-\frac{3}{4}$ inch and up) with prices per tree increasing from small to large caliper ones.

## INTERSTEM METHOD OF DWARFING

As previously mentioned, each rootstock clone has a built in mechanism for dwarfing. When a short stem-section from one of these rootstock clones is grafted between a vigorous root system and a variety, a certain dwarfing influence is imposed on the tree. The root system of such 3-component trees can be of seedling sort or one of the well anchored clones. When a dwarfing clone is used as the rootstock under an interstem tree, the dwarfing effects of both parts will function.

The length of the interstem can vary from as short as 1 inch to 12 or more inches. In recently published research, it was found that a 6-inch interstem was sufficient to dwarf varieties as much as they are dwarfed on the same root system (5). It was also found that the most efficient interstem materials, considering dwarfing and production, were EM VIII, EM IX, and EM VII (Fig. 5).

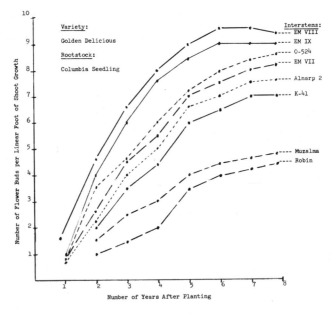

FIG. 5.

The practical significance of interstems for dwarfing is that the anchorage of the tree is improved—because a vigorous root system can be used. The dwarfing and precocity is induced in the variety depending on the interstem material used. The only disadvantage is the higher cost of producing the 3-component tree. The trees can be made by double grafting in the dormant season or by budding the rootstock with the interstem one year and then budding the variety on the interstem the second year. Where small self supporting trees are needed, double worked trees with either EM VIII or EM IX as the interstem, should be considered (Fig. 6).

## GENERAL PRACTICES WITH DWARFED TREES

*Scion Rooting.* Many trees on dwarfing rootstocks have become standard trees due to incorrect planting. The graft or bud union must remain above the soil line to keep the variety from sending out its own roots. In a study of scion rooting, in which the graft unions were purposely planted at different depths, it was found that when the graft union was 2 and 4 inches below the surface, scion roots occurred within 5 years (7). To prevent scion rooting, the graft union should be a minimum of 2 inches *above* the soil line.

*Tree Supports.* In general, the more dwarfing the rootstock, the more prone it is to induce trees to lean. This weakness is also associated with the wood structure of the rootstock. The wood of Em VIII and IX is brittle and breaks with stress. In addition, the root systems of these rootstocks are not as extensive as those of the more vigorous rootstocks. EM VII is prone to lean and "break off", however its wood is less brittle. The leaning is often due to a one sided root system.

The leaning of trees now is corrected to some extent by budding 14 to 16 inches high on the rootstock in the nursery. Then, these trees are planted 12 to 14 inches deeper in the orchard than they were in the nursery. New roots are formed on the rootstock shank in the soil to help anchor the trees. There is no particular anchorage problem with MM 106 and 111.

Many methods are used to support leaning trees. Any support from a stake to a wire trellis is sufficient, providing it does not interfere with orchard operations and is not expensive. A general rule is not to stake or support trees until there is a positive

FIG. 6.

need to do so. However, where the dwarf rootstocks are used for hedgerows, such as varieties on EM IX, a trellis system is required both for tree support and tree training. Various tree training systems have been described and therefore need not be covered here.

*The Virus Situation.* Many of the rootstock clones are being freed of the most dominant viruses by heat treatment and regular virus indexing programs. Eventually apple varieties, which carry latent viruses, will be checked in similar manner. The reduction of yield, if any, from latent viruses is not known. The stem pitting virus of Virginia Crab no doubt has some influence on tree growth and cropping; however, such severe symptoms are not apparent in the present clones (Fig. 7). Nurserymen are aware of the virus situation and, whenever possible, are obtaining virus tested clones and conforming to index programs.

Fig. 7.

## PERFORMANCE OF CERTAIN SCION ROOTSTOCK COMBINATIONS

Each particular apple variety will respond in its own manner to the rootstock on which it is budded or grafted. Certain varieties are best suited to specific rootstocks in degree of dwarfing, tree form, and production.

*Dwarfing Influence on Yield.* Since each variety inherently exhibits certain vigor and precocity characteristics, it follows that each rootstock also has its specific influence on that variety. In

some cases the rootstock influence may accentuate certain
behavior patterns of the variety and in other cases retard them.
For example, fruiting of Northern Spy on EM II can be a year
or two sooner than Northern Spy on EM VII; whereas fruiting
of McIntosh on EM II is often a year or two later than McIntosh
on EM VII.

The dwarfing characteristic is additive for the scion variety
and the rootstock, the more dwarfing the variety and the rootstock, the smaller the tree (Table 2). The same is generally true
for the fruiting and yield characteristics (precocity) of the variety and the rootstock. These factors must be taken into consideration in spacing trees in the orchard for efficient management.

*Tree Spacing.* The spacing of trees and the number of trees to
plant per acre is relative and depends on specific purposes such
as yield and mechanization. The preference of the owner and
his particular equipment and location also play a role. The trend
the past 20 years has been to reduce tree size and increase
number of trees per acre from 40 to 400. At the low number of
trees per acre, the more vigorous rootstocks will give the highest
production. But, at the high number of trees per acre, the real
dwarfing rootstocks are the most productive and should be
used. The same holds true for the vigor of the variety. Jonathan
on MM 106 can be spaced closer than Red Delicious on MM
106 under the same conditions. So then, special attention in
spacing of trees, is called to: 1. vigor of the variety and the
rootstock, 2. soil type and location, 3. training system, and 4.
owner perference. Tree spacings can be classified as to number
of trees/acre as follows: Low tree density 100 to 200 trees/acre;
medium density 300 to 600; and high density 600 to 1000
trees/acre.

For example free standing trees in the hedgerow system
would vary in tree number depending on the variety and the
rootstock used (Fig. 8). The maximum tree height in any type
of spacing should be about 14 feet and the tree spread at
maturity 10 feet at the bottom and 4 feet at the top. Such tree

Hedge-Row System

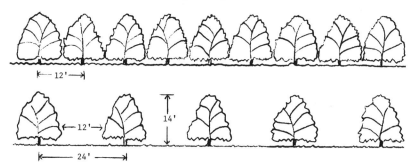

Off-Set Tree Spacing System

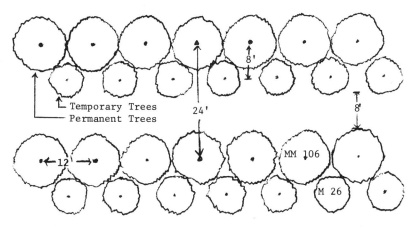

FIG. 8.

spacing lend itself to platform mechanical harvesting aids.

The off-set tree spacing system may be used to advantage in obtaining maximum yields per acre during the early life of the orchard. As an example, permanent trees are planted 12 x 24 feet and temporary trees are planted between the permanent trees but 8 feet to one side of the (Fig. 8). Again certain of the dwarfing rootstocks are suited to this use. For example, under good soil type the permanent varieties could be on EM VII, MM 106, or MM 111 and the off-set varieties on EM IX or EM 26. After 10 to 12 years, when trees become crowded, the off-set trees can be removed allowing more space for the permanent trees.

In the future, no doubt, the trees will be spaced in the orchard according to the use of the fruit. Fruit for the fresh market and storage will come from closely planted trees; and fruit for processing may come from trees adapted to the mechanical harvester systems.

*Rootstock Influence on Yield.* The yield per tree is influenced by the rootstock just as the yield per acre depends on the number of trees per acre. So to obtain maximum yields per acre, it is imperative to use precocious varieties on dwarfing rootstocks spaced at optimum number of trees per acre. Optimum trees per acre would be the number that can be grown efficiently from the standpoint of available light for the total leaf area. In other words, a point can be reached in spacing when shading may actually reduce yields due to height, spread and density of the trees.

Since yields vary from one orchard to another and from one fruit area to another, no specific yields per acre should be taken as normal. In high density plantings in Washington and Oregon, yields up to 3,000 loose boxes per acre have been reported. Documented and published yield data are not plentiful. Using four EM clonal rootstocks and two varieties (McIntosh and Red Delicious) it was demonstrated that clonal rootstocks outyielded the same varieties on seedling rootstocks over a 14-

year period (3). In a 35-year study in England certain rootstocks were more productive than others (12). In this 35-year period total yields of Worcester Pearmain varied from 6,000 to 11,000 bushels per acre for EM XVI (vigorous) and EM IX (dwarf) respectively.

Yields of two varieties on three rootstocks in Michigan varied in production according to variety, rootstock, and number of trees per acre (9). Production of these trees planted in 1945 varied in cumulative yield by 1958 from 600 to 1600 bushels per acre (Table 3). The most productive variety/rootstock combination was Corland/EM II.

TABLE 3.   Production of an orchard planted 1945, showing cumulative yields from 144 trees/acre (1947-1952) and from 72 trees/acre (1953-1958). No yields in 1955 due to frost

| Variety/ | Cumulative yields in bushels/acre | | |
|---|---|---|---|
| Rootstock | 144 trees/acre (1947-1952) | 72 trees/acre (1953-1958) | 14 year total |
| McIntosh/EM II | 1270 | 2919 | 4189 |
| McIntosh/EM VII | 1733 | 2745 | 4478 |
| McIntosh/EM XIII | 1235 | 3497 | 4732 |
| Cortland/EM II | 1728 | 3011 | 4739 |
| Cortland/EM VII | 1351 | 1796 | 3147 |
| Cortland/EM XIII | 932 | 2157 | 3089 |

In another similar study (Table 4) with EM rootstocks and four varieties, it was found that these variety/rootstock combinations outyielded the same varieties on seedling rootstock by two to five times (13).

Comparative production of varieties on the MM series of rootstock is rather limited. Unpublished yield performance or orchards planted in 1956 at East Lansing show certain trends. McIntosh/MM 106 produced the highest yield over the 11-

TABLE 4. Tenth year trunk circumference and cumulative yield from the fifth through the tenth years of four varieties and seven rootstocks planted in 1952 with 72 trees per acre

Cumulative yield (bushels per acre) (a) and trunk circumference (inches)

| Rootstocks | McIntosh | | Jonathan | | Red Delicious | | Northern Spy | |
|---|---|---|---|---|---|---|---|---|
| | Trunk circum-ference | Yield | Trunk circum-ference | Yield | Trunk circum-ference | Yield | Trunk circum-ference | Yield |
| EM I | 21.1 | 2572 | 19.0 | 2075 | 21.4 | 1571 | 20.1 | 995 |
| EM II | 19.0 | 2046 | 17.8 | 1902 | 21.6 | 1793 | 19.9 | 1382 |
| EM V | 19.0 | 1739 | 19.2 | 1618 | 20.7 | 1175 | 19.3 | 677 |
| EM VII | 16.7 | 1582 | 14.3 | 860 | 17.7 | 1370 | 18.0 | 1145 |
| EM XIII | 21.1 | 2154 | 18.8 | 1839 | 19.6 | 1056 | 20.0 | 282 |
| EM XVI | 20.9 | 1958 | 19.3 | 2455 | 20.8 | 1337 | 21.2 | 538 |
| Seedling (b) | .... | 524 | .... | 493 | .... | 393 | .... | .... |

(a) 42 pounds per bushel.

(b) The varieties on seedling rootstock were planted in 1949 at 54 trees per acre and were included here only to compare with dwarfing rootstock of comparable age.

year period, and for Red Delicious, EM II was the highest in production (Table 5). For Northern Spy, MM 104 was outstanding in yield, which may be attributed to the larger tree size of this combination.

In summary, the rootstock is a very influential part of the apple tree, but no one rootstock will serve all purposes. Selecting with much care is required. The rootstock can be considered as a biological control mechanism and, when used correctly, it can influence size of tree, flowering, fruit quality, and yield.

TABLE 5. Ten-year yields (bu./acre)[1] of 3 varieties on
6 rootstocks planted in 1956 at East Lansing,
at the rate of 100 trees per acre

| Variety/ Rootstock | | Yields in bushels per acre | | | | | | | |
|---|---|---|---|---|---|---|---|---|---|
| | | 1959 | 1960 | 1961 | 1962 | 1964 | 1965 | 1966 | 11-year total |
| McIntosh/MM | 104 | 8 | 40 | 58 | 160 | 530 | 180 | 730 | 1706 |
| McIntosh/MM | 106 | 13 | 45 | 103 | 133 | 938 | 179 | 1133 | 2544 |
| " /MM | 109 | 5 | 20 | 110 | 125 | 615 | 143 | 790 | 1808 |
| " /MM | 111 | 8 | 22 | 30 | 83 | 520 | 193 | 700 | 1556 |
| " /EM | II | 20 | 22 | 28 | 108 | 513 | 40 | 770 | 1501 |
| " /EM | VII | 15 | 28 | 35 | 95 | 320 | 230 | 413 | 1136 |
| R. Del. /MM | 104 | — | 8 | 18 | 103 | 212 | 115 | 375 | 831 |
| " /MM | 106 | 20 | 22 | 40 | 100 | 223 | 210 | 553 | 1168 |
| " /MM | 109 | — | 10 | 15 | 125 | 273 | 170 | 373 | 966 |
| " /MM | 111 | — | 15 | 35 | 89 | 138 | 100 | 285 | 662 |
| " /EM | II | 8 | 22 | 20 | 133 | 258 | 380 | 413 | 1234 |
| " /EM | VII | 22 | 20 | 48 | 115 | 180 | 180 | 380 | 945 |
| N. Spy /MM | 104 | — | 8 | 15 | 35 | 258 | 218 | 638 | 1172 |
| " /MM | 106 | — | 20 | 25 | 58 | 230 | 45 | 390 | 768 |
| " /MM | 109 | — | — | 10 | 11 | 140 | 38 | 230 | 429 |
| " /MM | 111 | — | — | 8 | 10 | 145 | 30 | 180 | 373 |
| " /EM | II | — | 22 | 30 | 83 | 345 | 82 | 403 | 965 |
| " /EM | VII | — | 15 | 10 | 30 | 148 | 80 | 180 | 463 |

[1] One bushel = 40 lb. Data converted from pounds per tree to bushels per tree.
No yield in 1963 due to frost.

# Literature Cited

1. Ashiru, G. A. and R. F. Carlson. 1967. Some factors involved in root induction of East Malling II and Malling Merton 106 apple clones. Ph.D. thesis, Department of Horticulture, Michigan State University.

2. Awad, Marcel M. and A. L. Kenworthy. 1963. Clonal rootstock, scion variety and time of sampling influence in apple leaf composition. Proc. Amer. Soc. Hort. Sci. 83:#68–73.

3. Brase, K. D. and R. D. Way. 1959. Rootstocks and methods used for dwarfing fruit trees. N.Y. St. Agr. Exp. Sta. Bull. 783.

4. Carlson, R. F. 1967. Growth response of several rootstocks to soil moisture. HortScience 2(3):108–110.

5. Carlson, R. F. 1965. The effects and relationships of intermediate

stem sections on growth and behavior of apple cultivars. Proc. Amer. Soc. Hort. Sci. 87:#21–28.

6. Carlson, R. F. 1966. Factors influencing root formation in hardwood cuttings of fruit trees. Mich. Agr. Exp. Sta. Quart. Bull. 48:#449–454.

7. Carlson, R. F. 1967. The incidence of scion-rooting of apple cultivars planted at different soil depths. Hort. Res. 7:#67–71.

8. Carlson, R. F. and H. B. Tukey. 1955. Cultural practices in propagation of dwarfing rootstocks in Michigan. Mich. Agr. Exp. Sta. Quart. Bull. 37:#492–497.

9. Carlson, R. F. and H. B. Tukey. 1959. Fourteen year orchard performance of several apple varieties on East Malling rootstocks in Michigan (second report). Proc. Amer. Soc. Hort. Sci. 74:#47–53.

10. Delap, Anne V. and Elsie M. Ford. 1958. Studies in nutrition of apple rootstocks. Ann. Bot. N. S. 22:#137–158.

11. Heinicke, D. R. 1963. The micro-climate of fruit trees. II. Foliage and light distribution patterns in apple trees. Proc. Amer. Soc. Hort. Sci. 83:#1–11.

12. Preston, A. P. 1959. Apple rootstock studies: Thirty five years' results with Worchester Pearmain on clonal rootstocks. J. Hort. Sci. 34:#32–38.

13. Toenjes, Walter and R. F. Carlson. 1963. Ten year performance of four apple varieties on six East Malling rootstocks. Mich. Agr. Exp. Sta. Quart. Bull. 45:#450–454.

14. Tukey, H. B. 1964. Dwarfed fruit trees. The MacMillan Company, N.Y. 562 p.

15. Upshall, W. H. 1943. Malling stocks and French Crab seedlings as stocks for five varieties of apples III. Aci. Agr. 23:# 537–545.

16. Witfield, A. B. 1965. The effect of stock and scion on the mineral composition of apple leaves. Rep. E. Malling Res. Sta. 1964:107–109.

# XIII. APPLE ORCHARDS OF TOMORROW

H.A. ROLLINS, Jr., Head
Department of Horticulture,

Virginia Polytechnic Institute,
Blacksburg, Virginia

THE ORCHARDS OF TOMORROW ARE BEING PLANNED WITH care today. Successful orchard operations do not just happen. They are developed after many long hours of detailed study and deliberation. Specific objectives and goals must be well defined before the first tree is placed in the soil.

There has been very little change in the orchards of America during the past century. The major advances in equipment, pesticides, growth regulating chemicals, fruit handling techniques, packing systems, and storages have come about with only slight modifications in the actual production unit, the tree. It is now apparent that during the next 25 years there will be significant changes in the orchard itself. These changes will be the result of attempts to solve some of the more critical problems facing the industry and to capitalize upon new technology.

Tomorrow's orchards cannot be precisely described. They will take on many different forms, since the conditions, objectives, and goals of one orchardist will vary from those of his neighbor. There are many factors—including potential market (fresh and processing), demand for quality, necessity for increased production efficiency, and diminishing supplies of qualified workers—that will influence future trends. All growers will not attempt to solve these problems in the same manner. In fact, there is no single road to success.

Apple orchards of tomorrow will reflect a gradual shift toward smaller trees, more closely spaced, and intensively managed. In some instances, they will be quite similar to present day orchards. In others, they will bear almost no similarity. The degree to which an individual grower will move toward highly intensive systems will be influenced by many factors, possibly the most important being his own progressive attitude and his willingness to try new and different concepts. In projecting the more advanced orchards of tomorrow three types are likely to dominate. For the sake of convenience they will be referred to as the "140 semistandard", the "240 compact", and the "440 hedge".

## "140 SEMISTANDARD"

The "140 semistandard" will be set at about 14 x 22 feet or 140 trees per acre. Tree height will be held to about 14 to 16 feet and diameter to about 14 feet. The trees will be either a spur type variety on a seedling rootstock or a standard form on a semidwarfing rootstock.

The system of training will be determined largely on the basis of whether the fruit is to be harvested with some form of shake and catch system or whether it will be removed by hand. If the fruit is to be harvested with a shake and catch system, the trees will be approximately circular when viewed from above. The lowest scaffold branches will be about 36 inches above the ground or high enough to facilitate the movement of equipment. They will likely be open center trees with scaffold branches spaced around the central shaft. Attempts will be made to avoid having a scaffold located in the path of fruits shaken from limbs above.

If the "140 semistandard" orchard is to be harvested by hand, then it is likely that the orchardist will start his lowest scaffold branched 14 to 16 inches above the ground and orient his main branches parallel to the tree row. Those scaffolds projecting into the row middles will be suppressed. The end result will be an oblong shaped tree when viewed from above, with the tree-row diameter twice that of the across the row diameter. Branches in the tree row will overlap slightly. Such plantings may be adapted to the use of platforms for harvest yet would not require the high degree of training necessary in the Italian Palmetto system where the trees are espaliered to a "fan" design on a wire trellis 12 to 14 feet high. The trees in such plantings should be kept sufficiently open to encourage fruiting to the center of the tree.

Trees larger than those described above will be found in some orchards but they will become the exception rather than the rule. The greater difficulty in harvesting fruit from large trees and the delay of such orchards in reaching their full production potential will discourage their development in the future.

## "240 COMPACT"

This design will be developed with still smaller trees more closely spaced and more intensively managed. The trees will be set at about 10 x 18 feet (240 trees per acre). They will be spur type varieties on either seedling or one of the semidwarfing clonal rootstocks, or standard scion varieties on one of the more size restricting rootstocks such as EM VII or MM 106. Such orchards will be designed to provide efficient hand harvest or some system other than shake and catch. The trees will be held to a height of about 10 to 12 feet with the principal scaffold limbs oriented parallel to the tree row. Bending and tying techniques to reduce the amount of pruning during early years will have considerable application in these plantings. If the trees are confined to a moderately narrow wall then the distance between the tree rows may be reduced. Once there is sufficient bearing surface per acre, probably in the fourth year, the planting will be allowed to bear. To induce fruiting, it is likely that the tree will have been scored, or sprayed with a growth regulating chemical the previous spring to initiate flower buds. To maintain compact plantings, it is likely that mechanical pruning with various arrangements of saws will be used. However, if such systems are used, "touch-up" pruning will be required. This may easily be done using power pruners from the picking platform. Workers pruning from a platform will be in a good position to make the best pruning decisions.

## "440 HEDGE"

This system will become more and more prevalent in the orchards of tomorrow if training costs do not prove excessive. Trees will be set 8 x 12 (440 trees per acre), or possibly even closer, and trained to a wire trellis. Four wires will likely be used, spaced so the lowest wire will be about 18 inches above the ground and the highest wire about seven feet. Branches will be tied to the wires which will serve mainly for training and to a lesser degree for support of the fruit. For such plantings the more drastic size controlling rootstocks will be used. In soils of high fertility EM IX may be considered. Rootstocks exerting somewhat less tree size restriction such as M 26 will likely be used in soils of moderate fertility. Spur type varieties on one of the semidwarfing rootstocks such as MM 106 may also have application in these plantings.

In working trees to a wire trellis, the principal training is done by bending and tying to the wires, cutting only when absolutely necessary. Considerable labor may be required to tie the trees during the first few years. However, once the basic framework is established tying becomes a minor operation. Pruning will consist of holding the trees within bounds and preventing them from becoming too dense.

Such a system has the potential of the earliest and heaviest production of any described. It permits the use of smaller, less costly spray equipment and reduces the waste of spray materials. It is also well adapted to efficient hand harvest and to improved fruit quality. The major question that will be answered in the development of the orchards of tomorrow is whether or not the increased cost of establishment, and the greater attention to detail required, will be offset by improved quality and reduced labor requirements. Such a system will have an important advantage in no ladder "pick your own" harvest systems where top quality is the goal of the orchardist.

Some high density plantings will be established without a trellis, each tree being staked and trained to a low "spindle bush". Such trees will be held to eight feet in height with two or three main scaffold limbs 18 to 24 inches above the ground with shorter fruiting laterals above.

In the development of the orchard of tomorrow there are many tools that may be used by the grower to mold his production unit to his own particular objectives. Some of these techniques are relatively new, most are not. However, it is important that the producer consider them only as tools and use them to his advantage to reach a desired goal. The skill of the grower in putting together these tools will likely determine his success. In the orchard of tomorrow the successful producer must be more of a student of horticulture than ever before.

## ROOTSTOCKS

One of the major tools that has not yet been fully explored in North America for the control of tree size is the rootstock for the specific soil, variety, and goal desired. In the orchard of tomorrow, widespread application will be made of various clonal rootstocks. They will be used as one of many tools by the orchardist to mold his planting to his specific goal. Rootstocks will not only be used to help regulate the size of the tree but also to provide for earlier production and, in some instances, to complement specific soil and environmental conditions.

In the development of the orchard of tomorrow more and more attention will be directed toward the selection and use of virus tested rootstocks as well as scion varieties. This will become an even more important consideration with the increased use of clonal rootstocks and the continued refinement of production techniques.

## TRAINING

In tomorrow's orchards greater attention will be given to specific tree training techniques in attaining desired goals. The specific methods to be used must be determined at the same time that design, rootstock, and spacing decisions are made, as all are interrelated. In plantings where shake-and-catch harvest systems are anticipated, the tree may be trained to an open center with limited laterals and sufficient clearance beneath the tree for the catching frame.

If hand harvest on small independent trees is planned, a central leader with a spiral of lateral branches, encouraged to develop spurs to the center of the tree, may be desired. If a hedge or trellis is planned, then possibly scaffolds developing other than parallel to the tree row should be suppressed to form a wall of bearing surface. In all systems, a technique to hold the trees within bounds should be devised and built into the plan. Trees should be held within prescribed bounds through the reduction of new shoot growth rather than to bring a tree back into bounds once it has extended beyond prescribed limits.

In tomorrow's orchards there will be greater application made of bending and tying techniques to minimize cutting, induce early fruiting, and direct branches to desired locations. Such systems require some form of trellis or stake. The growth of an individual branch can be regulated by the degree to which it is moved toward the horizontal. The more the orchardist wishes to suppress a strong, upright-growing lateral, the more it should be bent. Lateral branches should not, however, be pulled below the horizontal as this will depress terminal growth and force upright growing shoots to develop. While bending and tying techniques do involve considerable labor early in the development of the orchard, less work is required later to maintain the planting. A careful evaluation of the labor requirement within a specific situation is needed.

## FRUITING CONTROL

Fruiting control will be critical in the orchard of tomorrow. The fruiting of a tree will influence vegetative growth and, consequently, serve a useful purpose in size control. Growers will strive to first develop enough bearing surface per acre to make fruiting profitable and then stimulate the block into heavy fruiting. To fruit too early will delay the development of bearing surface and delay the time when maximum yields may be attained. To delay fruiting too long may result in a delay in profits and the production of too much vegetative growth.

A number of fruiting control techniques are available and, in the hands of a skilled orchardist, can be of immense value in developing an orchard. One such technique is the well established practice of "scoring". A cut is made through the bark to the wood and completely around the circumference of the trunk or main scaffold branches about ten days to two weeks after full bloom for the variety. This results in the initiation of flower buds for the following year. The orchardist must determine in the spring of one year whether there will be sufficient bearing surface the following year to make fruiting desirable. The use of the scoring technique often results in a more severe shock to the tree than is desirable. There are also growth regulating sprays that may be used to initiate flower buds. These sprays typically produce a less serious shock to the tree than scoring.

Also involved in the regulation of fruiting is the practice of fruit removal from trees that may set a crop before they have attained sufficient bearing surface to make fruiting profitable. Chemicals are used for this purpose. However, in the selection of a chemical to remove the fruit, care must be taken to avoid one that might result in a reduction in vegetative growth as this would defeat the purpose.

A somewhat more difficult phase of fruiting control is that of regulating the *amount* of fruit produced. The objective is to have enough fruit on the tree to provide the maximum amount of fruit per acre, without risking the chance of forcing the tree into an alternate bearing condition. If a tree is forced into fruiting and sets more fruit than would be desirable, some of that fruit must be removed. Frequently, the risk of overthinning with chemicals is less serious than the risk of having a new block develop an alternate bearing pattern.

## SCION VARIETIES

A tool that cannot be overlooked in the development of tomorrow's orchards is that of the growth characteristics of the scion variety. The trees of some varieties are smaller than others, some fruit earlier, some are more compact and heavier spur producers than others. The characteristics of the variety are involved in all other design considerations. The orchardist of tomorrow will be a student of variety characteristics and capitalize on the use of them.

## CHEMICALS

Several tools are already available to the producer in developing his orchard. Others will become available in the years to come. It is evident that the orchard of tomorrow will be developed with dependence upon chemicals and in particular growth regulating chemicals. It is now possible to modify vegetative growth, fruit firmness, fruit color, flower bud initiation, fruit thinning, fruit drop, and scald development through the proper and precise use of chemicals. Other potentials exist such as the delay of bloom, increase of blossom bud hardiness, and loosening the fruit from the spur for shake-and-catch harvest systems. The many uses of chemicals should be carefully assessed and every advantage taken of them in the development of the orchard of tomorrow. However, only approved chemicals should be applied and then only as recommended by competent advisors.

Extensive use will be made of leaf analysis as an index to fertilizer needs. Special attention will be paid to regulation of the tree's nitrogen supply, avoiding poor fruit color by too much and low yields by too little.

## PEST CONTROL

The control of insects, diseases, and rodents will continue to be an essential consideration in the orchard of tomorrow. However, greater emphasis will be placed upon biological means of restricting insect damage. Rodent populations will be reduced in order to minimize tree damage. Toxicants will still be required but they will be more specific in nature. Systemic fungicides will greatly alter spray programs. Spray and other equipment will be continually developed to satisfy the specific needs of the orchard rather than the orchard designed around available equipment. Smaller, lighter, less costly sprayers will be the rule with some indications that stationary systems may become practical. In the final analysis, the successful orchardist of tomorrow must either be a student of biological systems or have an authority in his employ or at his call. Pressure against the indiscriminate use of persistent toxicants will continue.

Breeding for resistance to apple scab *(Venturia inaequalis)* has made great strides in the hands of a few dedicated apple breeders and pathologists organized under the Apple Breeders' Cooperative (ABC) in U.S.A., England, and Canada. Most of the scab resistant selections have been developed from single-gene resistant parents. The most widely used are *Malus floribunda, M. prunifolia, M. micromalus, M. atrosanguinea.* There is evidence that one or more hitherto unknown races of apple scab may have cropped up. Most of the present scab-resistant ABC selections have commercial fruit size but are lacking in quality. Another back cross to commercial varieties is considered necessary. Disease and possibly insect resistant varieties will be valuable additions to the apple orchards of the future.

The orchards of tomorrow will reflect the influence of external factors—such things as consumer preferences, labor shortages, and modification in production economics to list only a few of the more significant. These influences will affect individual growers differently. Consequently, each will respond differently.

## MARKETS

Potential markets should be given first consideration in the design and development of a successful orchard operation. The producer must attempt to anticipate the variety and type of product that will be in greatest demand and return the highest profits 10 to 20 years ahead. This may or may not be what is currently in greatest demand. He may finally decide to grow for the fresh market, or for the processor. In some areas pick-your-own operations may present the greatest opportunity. Whatever the decision, it must be made before further plans are developed.

The production of apples for fresh consumption has long constituted the backbone of the industry and will continue to play a dominant role. To be successful, however, the grower must carefully analyze the demand of his consumers. He should then attempt to produce the variety and quality of fruit in demand. He should not attempt to compete with areas that have environmental or other advantages in the production of a specific variety unless he has a compensating advantage or needs the specific variety to maintain a desirable continuity of supply.

The trend is toward a higher proportion of the total national apple crop to be processed and offered to the consumer as a prepared product. This trend will continue. The decision to produce fruit for processing should be made prior to the setting of the orchard, and all plans then predicated on satisfying the specific requirements of that market. Only those varieties possessing the characteristics that best satisfy the needs of the processor and, likewise, those that can be grown most efficiently should be planted. The orchard should be designed to produce the greatest volume of fruit of the quality sought. Particular emphasis should be placed on minimizing per bushel costs. The potential for mechanical harvesting should also be given major consideration. In the future a higher proportion of the fruit utilized by apple processors will be grown in orchards designed for that specific purpose.

Another marketing system that requires an early decision is pick-your-own. In close proximity to expanding population centers, this type of operation can be very profitable and provide a practical solution to a diminishing supply of harvest labor. The decision to establish a pick-your-own operation should be made before the orchard is set, in order to arrange for parking, a convenient check out point, a sequence of varieties and small trees to either reduce or eliminate the need for ladders. All indications are that there are vast, undeveloped opportunities for this type of operation but it does require imagination and willingness on the part of the grower to revise his concepts of fruit production. It also requires a person with the ability, patience, and willingness to deal with the public.

## PRODUCTION EFFICIENCY

With the economic pressures which are now being exerted on the orchardist, only the most efficient will survive tomorrow's competition. Two important underlying factors in the efficient production of apples are high annual yields of quality fruit and early profitable production.

In recent years, production costs have risen sharply. Many of the routine expenses such as pruning, fertilizing, spraying, mowing, etc., are similar for each acre of orchard regardless of the size of the crop. As per-acre production is increased, the per-bushel production cost decreases. While high yields per acre are important to efficient production, there is a limit beyond which they can be projected without sacrificing fruit quality. In reality however, this level is seldom attained.

The orchard of tomorrow will be intensively managed to produce as high yields as practical without sacrificing fruit quality. Most systems will utilize closely spaced, smaller trees. Although the increasing value of land will be a factor in this trend, the dominant consideration will be that of reducing per-unit production costs.

A system of closely spaced, small trees facilitates a more rapid penetration of the soil with feeder roots and a more efficient use of the total soil area in the early years of the orchard. It also results in an earlier development of optimum bearing surface per-acre. These are important considerations as the grower attempts to minimize the time required to bring a new planting into profitable production and hastens returns on his capital investment.

The orchards of tomorrow will be developed on the basis of a shorter rotation system. Fewer orchards will be based on a 30- to 40-year life span. More and more will be brought into profitable production at the age of five years, fruited for an additional 10 to 20 years, and then replaced. A shorter rotational system will provide the producer the opportunity to minimize the hazard of variety obsolescence as well as to take full advantage of new production techniques.

In the development of more intensive systems of culture, sunlight is an important consideration. Every attempt will be made to insure that there be maximum foliage exposure to direct sunlight with a minimum of shading, either from one tree on another, or within an individual tree. Large spherical trees with an outer layer of fruiting surface and an extensive shaded nonproductive area will be phased out of tomorrow's orchards. They will be replaced with smaller trees in hedgerows thus giving a larger proportion of productive leaf surface per unit volume. The more uniform exposure of bearing surface to sunlight will also insure more uniform and higher quality fruit.

Under intensive production systems it will become more essential than ever before that the adverse influences of weather be minimized. Such systems require high levels of production every year to be profitable. Not only is the loss of the current crop important but the encouragement of biennial bearing and the loss of market continuity are also serious consequences.

Where high yield potentials exist, frost protection and irrigation systems that may have been of questionable value in the past will become highly important.

An important deterrent to high yields of quality fruit is low temperature in the spring. Spring freezes not only reduce or even eliminate the crop but, possibly of equal significance, is the adverse effect on fruit shape and finish. In the future, major emphasis will be placed on the elimination of this hazard.

Orchard sites with good elevation and air drainage will always be in top demand. However, in the future, various types of orchard heating systems will become more widely used. Principal emphasis will be placed on the efficiency of the system and labor saving considerations. More and more orchards will be established with permanent heating installations. With the refinement of these sytems, producers will begin to reassess the relative merits of a specific site, placing greater emphasis on such considerations as topography; adaptability to the use of equipment; depth, type, and fertility of the soil; and relative availability of water for moisture control. Desirable sites in every way, except for questionable air drainage, may be ideal orchard sites with maximum capacity for high yields of quality fruit *if* a practical and effective heating system can be incorporated into the operation. The advantages versus the disadvantages will be weighed carefully.

The lack of adequate soil moisture during critical periods is another factor that frequently limits the maximum productivity of an individual orchard. In the development of the orchard of the future, provision for supplemental water, when and where required, will be essential.

## LABOR

Possibly the major factor influencing the trend in tomorrow's orchards will be the limited availability of willing and qualified help, particularly harvest workers. Labor costs will increase as orchardists compete with other industries for competent workers. In order to provide the higher wages and various fringe benefits that will be required, the orchardist must develop his operation to make it possible for the worker to *earn* these higher wages for his employer. This will necessitate more mechanization to increase worker productivity. This trend will also create the need for more highly skilled workers to operate the more highly refined equipment.

Critical labor shortages will continue to develop during the harvest period, and, consequently, continued emphasis will be placed on the development and refinement of techniques to reduce harvest labor requirements. Tomorrow's orchards will be developed to provide maximum harvest efficiency. Significant progress is being made in the mechanical harvesting of apples. Further refinements will take place. Shake-and-catch harvest systems are practical for apples that are to be processed. Even for this purpose, however, bruising must be held to a minimum. Most of the bruising from shake-and-catch harvest occurs as the fruit falls through the tree, hitting branches and other fruits. Modifications in tree form and attention to pruning can improve the practicality of this system.

In orchards where shake-and-catch harvest systems are to be used, tree height should be held to 16 to 18 feet. It is also desirable to train trees to an open center with a limited number of major scaffolds spaced to avoid one developing immediately above another. Smaller trees also facilitate the use of smaller, more maneuverable catching-frame units that might also be adaptable to other tree fruit crops.

It is entirely possible that, with sufficient tree modification, shake-and-catch systems may ultimately be used to harvest apples for the fresh market, providing care in grading is exercised to eliminate seriously bruised fruit. However, quality of the product cannot be sacrificed if apples are to remain competitive with other commodities. It is for this reason that, where a quality product is sought, the human hand will be employed for many years to come in the actual detachment of the fruit from the spur. Orchards developed for the production of high quality fruit for fresh market will reflect modification to facilitate maximum efficiency in hand harvest.

Possibly the most efficient use of harvest workers will be to pick from a hedgerow where trees are set very close together and trained to a narrow wall, no deeper than two or three feet from limb ends to the trunk of the tree. Such walls could be seven feet in height if the worker were to remain with his feet on the ground, or it could be extended to a height of 12 to 14 feet if the worker were to harvest fruit from a low, slow-moving inclined-plane platform, possibly even fitted with a conveyor system to transport fruit to a bulk container.

With such a system, some producers may even find it practical for pickers to select or, spot pick only that fruit which falls within a given grade, size, and quality range. Some form of continuous shake-and-catch system could then be used to harvest the remainder for the processing market. In this way the producer would pick only fruit profitable for the fresh market and then send the remainder to the processor. The proportion harvested for each market would vary each year on the basis of the quality of the fruit and the strength of the respective markets. In the orchard of tomorrow no one harvest system will satisfy the requirements of all orchardists and two or more systems may be integrated and collectively utilized within an individual operation. An orchardist may also have more than one system of producing fruit for a specialized market.

In the design and development of tomorrow's orchards, consideration will be given to other sources of labor. Some orchardists may find it practical to use women on slow-moving, inclined-plane platforms. The work would be light as the fruit would be placed on a narrow conveyor in front of the picker. This same producer may find it practical to add lights to his unit and operate in the evening hours with persons seeking a few weeks extra work. Tomorrow's orchards will be developed to capitalize on whatever help may exist within the area.

While limited supplies of harvest workers will continue to be an important factor in the design and development of tomorrow's orchards, there will also continue to be a serious need to develop labor efficiencies in pruning. Consequently, in tomorrow's orchards more mechanical pruning equipment will be used. Several alternatives will undoubtedly emerge. One possibility would involve the use of completely mechanical systems such as the various forms of topping and hedging devices with a limited amount of touch up or follow up hand pruning. Another potential system, and probably one more consistent with the production of high quality fruit for the fresh market, would be the development of an orchard plan that would facilitate the use of power pruners on a moving platform, probably the same one used for harvest. In this way, high priced skilled labor could be used if they were sufficiently well trained and if the orchards were designed to make maximum use of such workers.

As in harvesting and pruning, orchardists will attempt to mechanize all phases of the orchard operation to insure that those workers employed will be able to *earn* the high wages they will demand. In planning the orchard of tomorrow growers should attempt to visualize ways of substituting machines for hand labor and ways of creating an environment that allows maximum efficiency from each worker. They need not design their orchard around specific and existing equipment shapes and sizes. If the demand develops for equipment modifications, they will be made.

## CONCLUSIONS

For the past century or more those advances that have taken place in the production of apples in North America have been the result of developing new equipment, chemicals, and techniques. However, in the next 25 years, significant changes will occur in both tree form and orchard design. These changes will be in the direction of smaller trees, closely spaced and intensively managed. They will be the result of attempts by producers to solve such problems as diminishing supplies of available and qualified labor, and rising per-acre production costs. In projecting his future, each grower must, on the basis of his own observations and predictions, plan the orchard of his tomorrow. Once he has determined the form, shape, and size of the trees that will best satisfy his needs then he must make his plans to reach that goal. Many tools are presently available such as growth regulating chemicals, size controlling rootstocks, new training techniques and redesigned equipment. While, in the past, major emphasis has been on the use of chemicals and machines, the future will require increased skills in the manipulation of plant growth. The orchardist of tomorrow must effectively mold the plant by the skillful use of available tools. For him the orchard of tomorrow is indeed fascinating.